TRENCHERMAN'S GUIDE

EDITION

27

Hotel Perfect
Hotel Management Software

Sharp's
BREWERY
ROCK • CORNWALL

TotalProduce

THE
WRECKING
COAST
DISTILLERY

salt

Salt, 5 Cross Street, Devon, EX31 1BA.
www.saltmedia.co.uk
01271 859299
ideas@saltmedia.co.uk

Written, designed and produced by Richard Bailey,
Nick Cooper, Sophie Chamier, Catherine Courtenay,
Sophie Ellis, Claire Fegan, Kate Fenton, Clare Hunt,
Kathryn Lewis, Tamsin Powell, Calandra Redfearn,
Jo Rees, Rosanna Rothery, Amy Sargeant,
Christopher Sheppard, Linda Weller and Selena Young.

Foreword

'Another year exploring the South West in pursuit of incredible edible adventures'

Since its inception 27 years ago, the *Trencherman's Guide* has held an unparalleled position in showcasing the most exceptional restaurants in the South West.

As you can see in this edition, the dining scene in the South West is world-class, so it's been our pleasure to create a guide that showcases the very best experiences at the very best establishments.

I hope you revel in exquisite and memorable moments at the places you encounter this year.

You'll also find special events and offers from the restaurants in our fortnightly email from Trencherman's HQ.

If you're not yet a member of the Trencherman's Club, do join as it costs nothing but is a treasure trove of exclusive must-dos. Visit www.trenchermans-guide.com to find out more, or see page 142.

Here's to another year exploring the South West in pursuit of incredible edible adventures.

Jo Rees
Editor

Contents

Nº**42**
Abbots Court

14   Welcome by Michael Caines MBE

16   2019 Trencherman's Awards

20   Using the guide

22   Gloucestershire

32   Wiltshire

42   Bristol & Bath

54   Somerset

64   Dorset & Hampshire

80   Devon

112   Cornwall

142   Join the club

144   Wine notes

150   Index

Welcome

'As a carefully curated collection
of top-rated restaurants,
the Trencherman's Guide is
a guarantee of exceptional
dining experiences'

I t's astonishing how the South West continues to evolve and shine as one of the UK's leading gastronomic regions.

The stunning seafood spoils plucked from the shimmering coastline, our long tradition of farming and careful animal husbandry, and our wealth of creative producers feeds a culture that's vibrant with food festivals, dining events, vineyards, world-class restaurants and food-focused hotels.

Recent innovations in the dining scene - which can be seen throughout this 27th edition - include the introduction of more plant-based eating experiences, a burgeoning proliferation of kitchen gardens and an explosion in craft distilling (and the innovative drinks experiences that result from it).

In an ever-changing environment, we restaurateurs and chefs continuously respond to customers' expectations - aiming, of course, to exceed them.

As a group of independent establishments, sourcing from many other small, independent and family-run businesses, we fly the flag for quality, authenticity and provenance, and strive to protect the natural landscape, push the boundaries of creativity and create experiences that are truly beautiful.

I hope you enjoy the guide.

Michael Caines MBE
Chairman of the Trencherman's committee

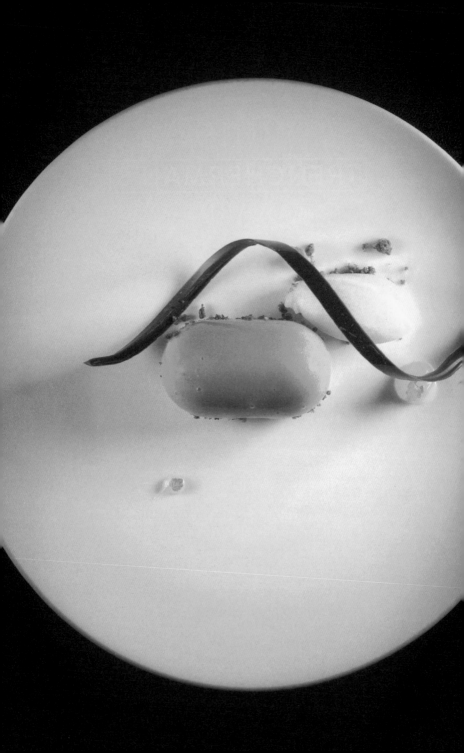

2019
TRENCHERMAN'S
AWARDS

Following the casting of more than 25,000 reader votes, the cream of the South West culinary crop were crowned at the 2019 Trencherman's Awards during a sumptuous ceremony at Saunton Sands Hotel in north Devon.

Chefs, restaurateurs, producers and others from the food, wine and hospitality industry attended the event and were treated to a fabulous four course feast. The dishes were crafted by last year's winners - Toby Gritten of The Pump House, Ben Palmer and Josh Ackland of Glazebrook House, and Tom Browning of Lewtrenchard Manor - as well as Andrea Santos, Mathias Oberg and the brigade from Saunton Sands Hotel who created this stunning dessert.

Discover who took home the prizes on the following pages and read more about the winners throughout the guide.

2019
Winners

BEST RESTAURANT

The Olive Tree Restaurant, Bath (Nº26)

BEST DINING PUB

Pyne Arms, north Devon (Nº88)

BEST CHEF

Jude Kereama, Kota, Porthleven (Nº128)

BEST FRONT OF HOUSE TEAM

The Coach House by Michael Caines, Kentisbury (Nº62)

BEST DINE AND STAY EXPERIENCE

The Idle Rocks, St Mawes (Nº120)

BEST BAR LIST

The Water's Edge at The Greenbank Hotel,
Falmouth (Nº121)

AWARD FOR CREATIVITY AND INNOVATION

Acorn Restaurant, Bath (Nº27)

Using the guide

To be included in the guide, all restaurants exceed a strict scoring criteria, so you can be confident they offer an exceptional dining experience.

Those that achieve an exceptionally high score have an image and longer description than the other high quality restaurants included.

Trencherman's Award winners can be identified as they feature as a whole page write-up.

To make the guide easy to use, the establishments are divided by geographic regions.

Each restaurant has a number which you'll also find on the map at the beginning of each region's section.

Look out, too, for these symbols as they'll provide even more information.

**Trencherman's
Award finalists**

**Restaurant
with rooms**

Left: wood pigeon, beetroot, walnut and sloe gin dish created by Toby Gritten of
The Pump House, Bristol, for the 2019 Trencherman's Awards dinner

Gloucestershire

Restaurants listed in the guide correspond to the
numbers plotted on the map

☐ Full member

☐ Standard member

1	Lords of the Manor Hotel
2	The Slaughters Manor House
3	The Painswick
4	The Old Passage
5	The Bell Inn
6	Wild Garlic
7	Wilder
8	Calcot & Spa
9	The Seagrave Arms
10	Koj

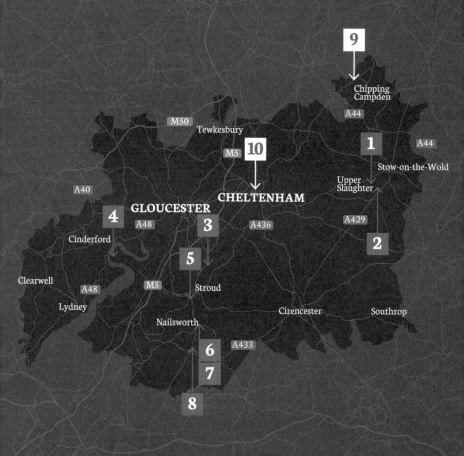

All locations are approximate

1 §

Lords of the Manor Hotel

Beautifully bijou

At this luxury hotel in serene Cotswolds countryside, it's a little too easy for visitors to feel like the real lord (or lady) of the manor.

A full refurbishment at the start of 2019 blended no-expense-spared glamour with the building's 17th century heritage, and also added a second restaurant.

At the intimate Atrium Restaurant, head chef Charles Smith continues to charm guests with innovative eight-course tasting menus. The new brasserie, The Dining Room, offers a more informal experience for guests staying a second night. A number of the beautiful bedrooms accommodate well-behaved dogs.

Chef **Charles Smith**
3 course lunch from **£27.50**
3 course dinner from **£35**
Seats **56**
Bedrooms **26**
Room rate from **£155**

Upper Slaughter, near Bourton-on-the-Water, Gloucestershire, GL54 2JD
01451 820243
www.lordsofthemanor.com

f @lordsofthemanorhotel
🐦 @cotswoldlords
📷 @lordsofthemanor

2 §

The Slaughters Manor House

Art and craft

This beautiful 17th century manor house in the heart of a Cotswolds village celebrates traditional heritage, while adding a generous dash of modernity.

Chef Nik Chappell seeks out the very best regional produce and combines classic, seasonal ingredients with more unusual, often foraged flavours to construct imaginative and innovative menus. The artful plating and creative combinations make sense when you know that Nik was originally set on a career in the arts before transferring his focus from paper to plate.

Indulge in an aperitif at the bar before dining in the smart restaurant.

Chef **Nik Chappell**
3 course lunch from **£30**
3 course dinner from **£67.50**
Seats **40**
Bedrooms **19**
Room rate from **£195**

Copsehill Road, Lower Slaughter, Gloucestershire, GL54 2HP
01451 820456
www.slaughtersmanor.co.uk

f @theslaughtersmanorhouse
🐦 @slaughtersmanor
📷 @brownswordhotels

3 S

The Painswick

Quality creds in the country

This stylish bolthole with fabulous valley views sits comfortably in its pretty Cotswold town setting. The house, originally built in the 18th century, got a chic makeover by its current owners before it opened three years ago as a restaurant with rooms.

Chef Jamie McCallum trained under Gary Rhodes and was latterly at Wild Honey in Mayfair and his quality creds show in food that's deliciously crowd pleasing while still being rather smart.

Expand your visit with pre-dinner cocktails in the glam bar or book the private dining area with its imaginative Feast menu and create a special event for friends and family.

Chef **Jamie McCallum**
3 course lunch from **£25**
3 course dinner from **£32**
Seats **60**
Bedrooms **16**
Room rate from **£196**

Kemps Lane, Painswick, Gloucestershire, GL6 6YB
01452 813688
www.thepainswick.co.uk

f @thepainswickhotel
🐦 @the_painswick
📷 @the_painswick

4 S

The Old Passage

Piscatorial feasting

Freshly shucked oysters, grilled lobster bathed in garlic butter and an assembly of seafoods piled high in the signature fruits de mer: dinner at this riverside restaurant is a sanctuary for piscatorial pleasure seekers.

Positioned on the banks of the Severn and looking out onto the Forest of Dean, The Old Passage is one of Gloucestershire's best kept secrets. Foodies in-the-know flock here for their fix of freshly landed fish sourced each morning from Devon and Cornwall dayboats.

In summer, light and airy decor lends the dining room a Mediterranean feel – toast your good fortune in discovering this fabulous find with a couple of glasses of chilled fizz.

Chef **Lewis Dixon**
3 course lunch from **£22.50**
3 course dinner from **£35**
Seats **40**
Bedrooms **2**
Room rate from **£100**

Passage Road, Arlingham, Gloucestershire, GL2 7JR
01452 740547
www.theoldpassage.com

f @theoldpassage
🐦 @oldpassageinn
📷 @the_old_passage

5 S A
The Bell Inn
Cotswolds weekender

Gin connoisseurs should earmark this Cotswolds inn for an overnight visit, as its bar boasts an impressive collection of over 90 gins – earning the 16th century pub a place in the *South West Independent Gin Guide*.

While the spirit list ventures far and wide, The Bell's food offering rarely strays far from its Gloucestershire roots. Locally-shot game, ocean-fresh fish and seasonal vegetables feature on chef patron Mark Payne's menu. House favourites include pressed ham hock and a guinea fowl terrine with chicken liver parfait.

Chef **Mark Payne**
3 course lunch from **£29**
3 course dinner from **£29**
Seats **58**
Bedrooms **2**
Room rate from **£75**

Bell Lane, Selsley, Gloucestershire, GL5 5JY
01453 753801
www.thebellinnselsley.com

f @thebellatselsley
🐦 @bellinnselsley
📷 @bellinnselsley

6 S
Wild Garlic
Crowd–pleasing plates

Gorgeous country-chic bedrooms, a sleepy market town setting and lazy brunches of locally laid eggs, proper sourdough and bloody marys ... weekends away with someone special don't get much more delightful than those at Wild Garlic.

Crowd-pleasing plates at the neighbourhood bistro are dictated by the season but stalwarts include slow-cooked brisket tagliatelle and whole grilled Brixham plaice.

Make it a two-day getaway so you can also fit in a visit to sample the innovative cooking at sister restaurant Wilder across the road.

Chef **Matthew Beardshall**
3 course lunch from **£29**
3 course dinner from **£29**
Seats **44**
Bedrooms **5**
Room rate from **£80**

3 Cossack Square, Nailsworth, Gloucestershire, GL6 0DB
01453 832615
www.wild-garlic.co.uk

f @wildgarlicnailsworth
🐦 @thewildgarlic
📷 @wildgarlicnailsworth

7 🅐
Wilder
New wave fine dining

After putting Nailsworth on the culinary map when he launched his first restaurant, Wild Garlic, seasoned chef Matthew Beardshall then went and doubled the market town's culinary credentials when he launched sister venue Wilder in 2017.

As the name suggests, the second venture is an untamed take on the original neighbourhood bistro; the ambitious chef's ingenuity is unleashed on adventurous diners via a surprise tasting menu. While the vibe is relaxed, each dish on the daily changing eight course line-up is an impressive collision of taste, texture and skill. For the full experience, don't eschew the optional wine flight.

Chef **Matthew Beardshall**
8 course tasting menu **£70**
Seats **22**

Market Street, Nailsworth, Gloucestershire, GL6 0BX
01453 835483
www.dinewilder.co.uk

f @wilder
🐦 @dinewilder
📷 @dinewilder

8 🆂
Calcot & Spa
Cotswold chic

This beautiful, honey-coloured stone manor house, set in 220 acres of Cotswold meadows, is an idyllic dining location.

The main building dates back to the 14th century, but the modern Conservatory restaurant provides a stunning light-filled backdrop for head chef Richard Davies' creative and extremely accomplished cooking (there's an equally adventurous wine and cocktail list).

For more informal eating, try the Gumstool Inn within Calcot's grounds. The cosy village pub is perfect for a relaxed evening of comfort food by the fire. On warm evenings, wander outside to the lavender-lined courtyard and dine alfresco.

Chef **Richard Davies**
3 course lunch from **£25**
3 course dinner from **£42**
Seats **60**
Bedrooms **35**
Room rate from **£219**

Near Tetbury, Gloucestershire, GL8 8YJ
01666 890391
www.calcot.co

f @calcotandspa
🐦 @calcotandspa
📷 @calcot_and_spa

Gloucestershire

The Seagrave Arms

Even the most seasoned diners crave comfort and familiarity from time to time, and the unfussy food at this Cotswolds inn hits the spot without skimping on quality.

Local farmers and producers stock the kitchen with impeccably fresh produce which the team mindfully manipulate into dishes such as whisky and marmalade glazed ham hock, and smoked haddock fishcakes.

Located just 20 minutes from the Cotswolds Distillery, it's also a fabulous spot to enjoy locally crafted gin.

Chef **Chris Ellis.** 3 course lunch from **£19.95.** 3 course dinner from **£35.** Seats **30.** Bedrooms **8, plus a 2 bed cottage.** Room rate from **£100**

Friday Street, Chipping Campden, Gloucestershire, GL55 6QH 01386 840192 **www.seagravearms.com**

f @theseagravearms
🐦 @theseagravearms
📷 @theseagravearms

Koj

Opened in 2017 by *MasterChef* finalist Andrew Kojima, Koj's no-sushi policy promises diners an alternative taste of Japanese cuisine. An open kitchen adds a touch of theatre to the cosy and informal dining space where you can sample steamed buns, grazing dishes, sides and soups.

Before - or after - dinner, head upstairs to the Bandana Monkey bar for craft beers, sake, shochu and Japanese whisky, as well as Asian inspired cocktails such as an Okinawa Old Fashioned or a Mitsubatchi.

Chefs **Andrew Kojima and Robin Stock.** 3 course dinner from **£20.** Seats **32**

3 Regent Street, Cheltenham, Gloucestershire, GL50 1HE 01242 580455 **www.kojcheltenham.co.uk**

f @kojcheltenham
🐦 @kojcheltenham
📷 @kojcheltenham

Chris Staines
The Ollerod (Nº44)

'I'm excited about getting out to see more of what the South West has to offer. I'm planning to go to Abbots Court (Nº42) soon. It looks stunning - and the food delicious.'

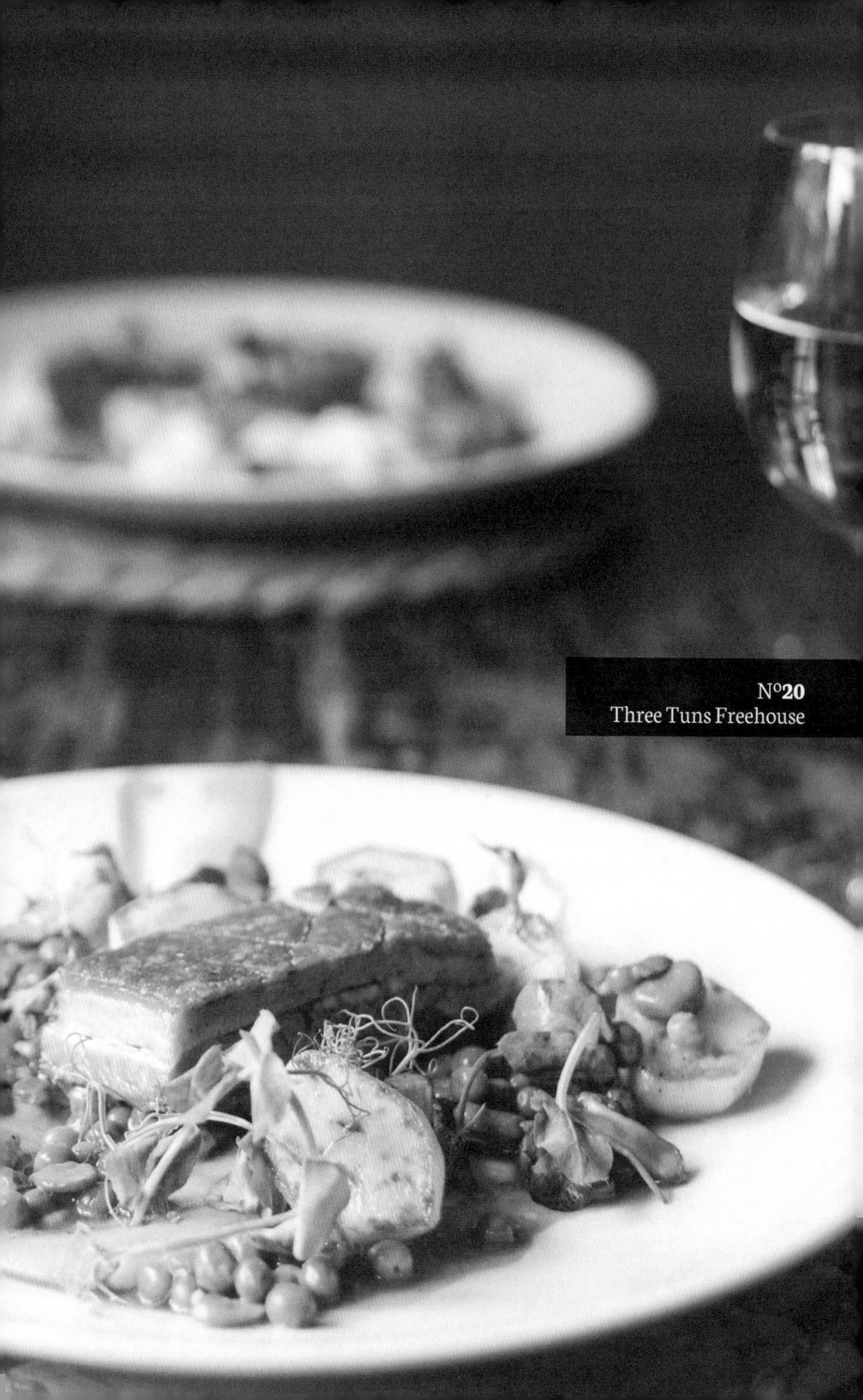

Nº**20**
Three Tuns Freehouse

Wiltshire

Restaurants listed in the guide correspond to the
numbers plotted on the map.

 Full member

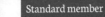 Standard member

11   Lucknam Park Hotel & Spa

12   The Methuen Arms

13   The White Horse Inn

14   The Bell

15   The Peppermill

16   Howard's House Hotel

17   The Bunch of Grapes

18   The George at Woolley

19   Lansdowne Strand

20   Three Tuns Freehouse

21   Anokaa Restaurant

All locations are approximate

11 S

Lucknam Park Hotel & Spa

Palladian perfection

From the tree-lined drive and Palladian mansion to the award winning spa and 500 acres of grounds, Lucknam Park has all the elements of a very special country house hotel – and then some. And thanks to the in-house cookery school, you can even upgrade your culinary skills on your visit.

Lucknam's fine dining has come with a Michelin star for the past 14 years and executive chef Hywel Jones keeps the standards tip-top in both the main restaurant and The Brasserie.

Start with cocktails in the magnificent drawing room before feasting on à la carte or signature tasting menus crafted from local and kitchen garden ingredients.

Chef **Hywel Jones**
3 course lunch from **£45**
3 course dinner from **£87**
Seats **64**
Bedrooms **42**
Room rate from **£295**

Colerne, Wiltshire, SN14 8AZ
01225 742777
www.lucknampark.co.uk

f @lucknampark
🐦 @lucknampark
📷 @lucknam_park

12 S A

The Methuen Arms

Nose–to–tail dining

This restored Georgian inn in the village of Corsham continues to surprise and delight.

From the buzz of the bar area through to the stylish restaurant, there's a lively and welcoming atmosphere. It's an energy which is reflected in chef Leigh Evans' menu of innovative dishes and classic pub favourites.

After sourcing produce from the surrounding landscape, Leigh crafts everything in-house and in accordance with his nose-to-tail cooking philosophy.

Book a room and, after a champion breakfast, head out to explore the neighbouring stately home of Corsham Court.

Chef **Leigh Evans**
3 course lunch from **£29.50**
3 course dinner from **£29.50**
Seats **120**
Bedrooms **19**
Room rate from **£140**

2 High Street, Corsham, Wiltshire, SN13 0HB
01249 717060
www.themethuenarms.com

f @themethuenarms
🐦 @methuenarms
📷 @themethuenarms

The White Horse Inn

Foodie adventures in Wiltshire

Having recently earned a second AA rosette and an official entry in the *Michelin Guide 2019*, the success of this rural Wiltshire dining inn continues to flourish.

Head chef Ben Reid and team deliver well-executed pub classics prepared with thoughtfully sourced seasonal produce, while the cosy bar is renowned for its locally brewed real ales and craft ciders.

Stay in one of eight delightfully appointed rooms (most of which overlook the pub gardens and paddock) to explore the magnificent Wiltshire countryside and nearby towns of Marlborough, Chippenham and Bath.

Chef **Ben Reid**
3 course set lunch from **£15**
3 course dinner from **£24**
Seats **40**
Bedrooms **8**
Room rate from **£75**

Compton Bassett, Calne, Wiltshire, SN11 8RG
01249 813118
www.whitehorse-comptonbassett.co.uk

f @whitehorsecb
🐦 @whitehorsecb
📷 @whitehorsecomptonbassett

The Bell

Hitting the right note

This 300-year-old former coaching house has appeal in spades. Part of the Ramsbury Estate (which has its own brewery, distillery and smokehouse) it was awarded AA Hospitality Pub of the Year England 2017-2018, offers nine sumptuous en-suite rooms and serves an enticing menu of modern British classics.

Under head chef Oly Clarke, the kitchen creates stunning dishes inspired by local produce. Many of the seasonal ingredients come straight from the kitchen garden or are sourced from the Estate. Experience them in exquisite fare such as the Estate game terrine and Ramsbury Gin cured salmon.

Chef **Oly Clarke**
3 course lunch from **£29**
3 course dinner from **£29**
Seats **44**
Bedrooms **9**
Room rate from **£110**

The Square, Ramsbury, Marlborough, Wiltshire, SN8 2PE
01672 520230
www.ramsbury.com

f @thebellramsbury
🐦 @thebellramsbury
📷 @bell_ramsbury

Take 5
GLAMOROUS WEEKENDS
Pack your glad rags for a glittering getaway

The Slaughters Manor House

Sublime eating is paired with effortless glamour in the Gloucestershire countryside.

Lympstone Manor

Michael Caines' jewel-box manor house delivers Michelin starred dining, luscious decor and a newly planted vineyard.

Chewton Glen Hotel & Spa

Modern British cooking comes with optional sides such as treehouse accommodation, spa, tennis centre and the James Martin Cookery School.

Lucknam Park Hotel & Spa

Luxuriate in a rural escape from the bustle of nearby Bath at this Palladian mansion with Michelin starred dining and spa.

The Nare

Sherry decanters in the bedrooms and private motor-launch picnics hint at the fabulous old-fashioned elegance to be found at this beachside hotel.

15 S
The Peppermill
Modern British cooking

A contemporary best-of-British menu, dedicated wine bar and seven beautifully furnished bedrooms make The Peppermill a tempting proposition for a greedy weekend in Wiltshire.

The smart restaurant with rooms, which sits at the heart of the lively market town of Devizes, has gained an enviable reputation for its 150-strong wine list, accomplished cooking and prolific use of local and seasonal produce. Drop in at lunchtime for classics such as lamb's liver and bacon, or hold out until dinner and get stuck into the cocktail list and full à la carte feasting.

Chef **Leon Sheppard**
3 course lunch from **£20**
3 course dinner from **£30**
Seats **65**
Bedrooms **7**
Room rate from **£95**

40 St John's Street, Devizes, Wiltshire, SN10 1BL
01380 710407
www.peppermilldevizes.co.uk

f @peppermilldevizes
🐦 @peppermilldev
📷 @peppermilldevizes

16 S
Howard's House Hotel
Romantic rural retreat

This charming country house hotel in a 17th century building has earned itself a number of honourable mentions as one of the most romantic getaway spots in the country.

As the hotel is surrounded by rolling Wiltshire countryside and farmland, head chef Andy Britton is somewhat spoilt for choice of local suppliers - he even has seasonal veggies grown in the kitchen garden at his disposal.

Taste the terroir in an ambitious menu which curates dishes such as scallop ceviche with lime, lemon balm and horseradish. Intrigued foodies can also sign up to one of Andy's masterclasses which often include a guided tour of the garden.

Chef **Andy Britton**
Lunch plates from **£7.95**
3 course dinner from **£33.50**
Seats **22**
Bedrooms **9**
Room rate from **£150**

Teffont Evias, Salisbury, Wiltshire, SP3 5RJ
01722 716392
www.howardshousehotel.co.uk

f @howardshousehotel
🐦 @howards_house
📷 @howardshouse_hotel

Wiltshire

17

The Bunch of Grapes

The pairing of polished pub classics with a more refined menu makes this contemporary meeting place a pleasing choice for all manner of occasions.

Chef patron Tony Casey's modern British approach and keen eye for creativity ensures that fish and chip lunches are as interesting as smart suppers of torched and cured salmon with brassicas and mooli.

Toast the evening with one of the expertly crafted cocktails before diving into dinner and exploring the diverse wine list.

Chef **Tony Casey.** 3 course lunch from **£22.50.** 3 course dinner from **£35.** Seats **80**

14 Silver Street, Bradford-on-Avon, Wiltshire, BA15 1JY
01225 938088
www.thebunchofgrapes.com

f @thegrapesboa
🐦 @thegrapesboa
📷 @thegrapesboa

---

18 🅂

The George at Woolley

Curl up on a cosy Chesterfield in front of the fire and sip real ale or a local artisan gin before investigating one of the four dining areas (plus a private dining room) at this delightful country pub run by chef Alex Venables and Alison Ward-Baptiste.

The classic British menu changes daily (depending on what local produce arrives at the kitchen door) and includes game, homemade breads and sumptuous desserts. Georgian bedrooms – given a contemporary twist – make stopping over an enticing proposition.

Chef **Alexander Venables.** 3 course lunch from **£17.95.** 3 course dinner from **£20.95.** Seats **90.** Bedrooms **2.** Room rate from **£110**

67 Woolley Street, Bradford-on-Avon, Wiltshire, BA15 1AQ
01225 865650
www.thegeorgebradfordonavon.co.uk

f @thegeorgeatwoolley
🐦 @thegeorgeatboa
📷 @thegeorgeatwoolley

19 S

Lansdowne Strand

This Grade II-listed coaching inn has provided comfortable beds and sustenance for weary travellers passing through Calne for nearly 500 years, and for the last decade has been owned by Arkell's Brewery.

However, while Lansdowne Strand revels in its history, the hotel's 25 handsomely decorated bedrooms and two AA rosette restaurant cement its status as a contemporary retreat. Sustainable sourcing comes high on head chef Joel Lear's agenda and most of the meat on the concise menu is reared in Wiltshire - the bacon and charcuterie is cured just down the road at Buttle Farm.

Chef **Joel Lear.** 3 course lunch from **£19.50.**
3 course dinner from **£28.** Seats **50.** Bedrooms **25.**
Room rate from **£75**

The Strand, Calne, Wiltshire, SN11 0EH
01249 812488
www.lansdownestrand.co.uk

f @lansdownestrand
𝕏 @lansdownestrand
◎ @lansdowne_strand

20

Three Tuns Freehouse

Great Bedwyn residents regularly toast their luck that James and Ashley Wilsey took over their village inn in 2012.

Returning to his Wiltshire roots after a successful career in London, chef patron James introduced a crowd-pleasing menu which riffs on pub classics - think crispy whiting goujons, unctuous wild boar ragu and apple nut crumble.

Charm is worn into the woodwork of this rural find; bring your chums, unwind with a pint of local ale and revel in a long and lazy supper.

Chef **James Wilsey.** 3 course lunch from **£26.**
3 course dinner from **£26.** Seats **48**

1 High Street, Great Bedwyn, Marlborough,
Wiltshire, SN8 3NU
01672 870280
www.tunsfreehouse.com

f @threetunsfreehouse
𝕏 @threetunsbedwyn
◎ @three_tuns_bedwyn

21

Anokaa Restaurant

Central Salisbury is home to some decidedly contemporary Indian dining, thanks to the menu of adventurous meat, fish and veggie dishes at Anokaa.

Traditional Asian flavours and techniques are brought bang up-to-date by chef Paban Kumar Bhaniya Chhetri's innovative approach and clever spicing, with western influences layering on complexity.

Enjoy the restaurant's regular entertainment while savouring Chardonnay-soaked crispy duck breast, or play it safe with well-loved Indian classics.

Chef **Paban Kumar Bhaniya Chhetri.**
3 course lunch from **£8.95.** 3 course dinner
from **£25.50.** Seats **120**

60 Fisherton Street, Salisbury, Wiltshire, SP2 7RB
01722 414142
www.anokaa.com

f @anokaasalisbury
𝕏 @anokaasalisbury

Bristol & Bath

Restaurants listed in the guide correspond to the
numbers plotted on the map.

 Full member

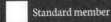 Standard member

22	The Spiny Lobster Grill
23	Mint Room - Bristol
24	Harvey Nichols Second Floor Restaurant
25	The Bath Priory
26	The Olive Tree Restaurant
27	Acorn Restaurant
28	Dan Moon at The Gainsborough
29	Mint Room - Bath
30	Menu Gordon Jones

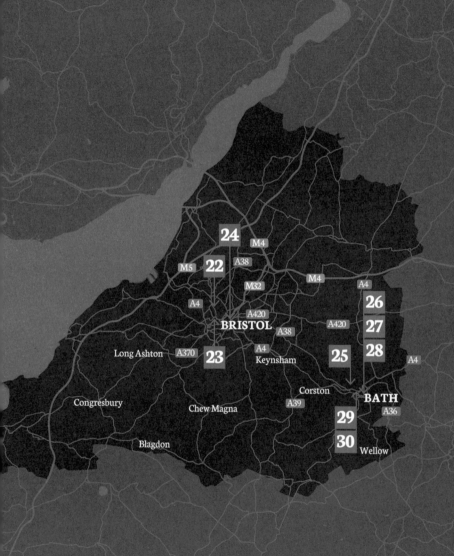

All locations are approximate

Take 5

SMALL AND SELECT

Intimate dining in beautifully bijou establishments

Outlaw's Fish Kitchen

Creative small plates of sparklingly fresh seafood are served in a fisherman's cottage setting at Port Isaac.

Oliver's

Quality cooking at Ken and Wendy's warmly inviting Falmouth find.

The Shore Restaurant

Bruce Rennie's Penzance restaurant is a must-visit for its reassuringly restrained bill of daily landed seafood.

Tabb's Restaurant

Nigel Tabb delights a small audience with memorable dishes at his Truro city centre restaurant.

Lords of the Manor Hotel

The newly created 14-cover fine dining Atrium Restaurant at Lords of the Manor Hotel lets chef Charles Smith's creativity fly.

22
The Spiny Lobster Grill
Mitch Tonks' city spot

A slick city restaurant may not be the first place you'd expect to find some of the best seafood in the South West but this Bristol brasserie excels in piscatorial pleasures and even has its own fishmonger selling the latest catch from Devon and Cornwall.

The fish focused menu (there are a few meaty options for land lubbers) is peppered with Mediterranean flavours and a number of the dishes are cooked over open flame care of the Josper oven.

Clash forks with your dining partner as you share dishes of plump scallops and whole monkfish tails dripping in garlic butter. The set dinner menu (served Tuesday to Thursday) is particularly good value.

Chef **Charlie Hearn**
3 course lunch from **£50 (£18 set menu)**
3 course dinner from **£50 (£18 set menu)**
Seats **43**

128-130 Whiteladies Road, Clifton, Bristol, BS8 2RS
01179 737384
www.thespinylobster.co.uk

f @thespinylobster
🐦 @_spinylobster
📷 @thespinylobster

23
Mint Room – Bristol
Creative Indian cooking

Executive chef Saravanan Nambirajan has redefined Indian dining in Bristol from the smart suburb of Clifton. Using his Michelin experience to marry traditional Asian flavours with contemporary cooking methods, Saravanan's tasting menus are a delightful culture clash of culinary creativity.

An extensive à la carte offering enables diners to map their own taste and texture journey, and vegetarian, gluten-free and vegan menus mean diners of all persuasions can get stuck in. An attractive blend of exposed bricks and luxe furnishings create a handsome setting in which to sip an aperitif before indulging in dishes such as southern spiced lobster with missi roti, and slow cooked Wiltshire lamb shank with caramelised onion and gold leaf.

Chef **Saravanan Nambirajan**
3 course lunch from **£22.95**
3 course dinner from **£30**
Seats **68**

12-16 Clifton Road, Bristol, BS8 1AF
01173 291300
www.mintroom.co.uk

f @mintroomclifton
🐦 @themintroom
📷 @themintroom

24

Harvey Nichols Second Floor Restaurant

City-style chic

Internationally-inspired dishes tempt destination diners to Harvey Nichols Second Floor Restaurant.

Long-standing head chef Louise McCrimmon crafts seasonal delights such as double baked soufflé, braised pork cheek and grilled Brixham plaice, which are served in a luxe dining room which shimmers with gold.

Start your visit at the sister bar next door for an aperitif cocktail and do the experience in style.

Chef **Louise McCrimmon**
3 course lunch from **£25**
3 course dinner from **£25**
Seats **65**

Harvey Nichols Bristol, 27 Philadelphia Street, Bristol, BS1 3BZ
01179 168898
www.harveynichols.com

f @harveynichols
y @harveynichols
@harveynichols

25 S A

The Bath Priory

Elegance in the city

Just a short walk from the bustling heart of Bath, this Georgian house (surrounded by four acres of award winning gardens), is a beautiful setting for an exemplary dining experience.

Executive chef Michael Nizzero - formerly premier sous chef at The Ritz (when it achieved its first Michelin star) - uses produce from the enviable kitchen garden to create modern, French-style menus.

Dine in luxury in the elegant restaurant or stop off during a shopping trip for coffee, lunch or afternoon tea at the more casual Pantry. Both dining areas have garden views and there's a terrace for pre-dinner drinks or alfresco eating. The excellent wine list is worth exploring, and vegetarians and vegans are well catered for too.

Chef **Michael Nizzero**
3 course lunch from **£35**
3 course dinner from **£85**
Seats **72**
Bedrooms **33**
Room rate from **£215**

Weston Road, Bath, Somerset, BA1 2XT
01225 331922
www.thebathpriory.co.uk

f @thebathpriory
y @thebathpriory
@brownswordhotels

The Olive Tree Restaurant

Luxurious Michelin finesse

With its newly acquired Michelin status, this restaurant beneath The Queensberry Hotel is one to seek out when visiting historic Bath.

Luxurious ingredients such as locally procured eel, veal, fallow deer and truffles are treated to the creative cooking and elegant plating of head chef Chris Cleghorn.

Relaxed glamour and refreshing informality (with a touch of quirk) are the hallmarks of this unique establishment set in a modernised medley of traditional Georgian townhouses.

Start your dinner experience with carefully crafted drinks in the Old Q Bar before heading down to The Olive Tree for superb tasting menus paired with fine wines. Owen Farr and the front of house team employ discerning skill and charm to ensure a fabulous foodie adventure.

Chef **Chris Cleghorn**
3 course lunch from **£32.50**
3 course dinner from **£60**
Seats **50**
Bedrooms **29**
Room rate from **£100**

The Queensberry Hotel,
4-7 Russel Street, Bath, BA1 2QF
01225 447928
www.olivetreebath.co.uk

f @olivetreebath
🐦 @olivetreebath
📷 @olivetreebath

Specialist ingredients, sourced by chefs for chefs

27

Acorn Restaurant

Gourmet vegan dining

Acorn may be set in a traditional panelled Georgian dining room in one of Bath's oldest buildings, but it's home to a fresh and inventive take on vegan dining which rewrites the rules on gourmet cooking sans-meat.

Plant-based eating is given a sumptuously elegant twist by chef patron Richard Buckley and chef Jamie Taylor who marry classical and innovative techniques, layering flavours and textures to remarkable effect. Try dishes like the intriguing radish sorbet or earthy mushroom parfait.

There's a well-considered drinks list - including some creative cocktails - to pair with the plates, and wines are thoughtfully matched to help swerve any decision-making dilemmas (vegan dining throws the red wine/red meat rule, of course). Opt for the tasting menu and accompanying wine flight to fully appreciate modern veganism at its most invigorating.

Chefs **Richard Buckley and Jamie Taylor**
3 course lunch from **£25.35**
3 course dinner from **£38.95**
Seats **32**

2 North Parade Passage,
Bath, BA1 1NX
01225 446059
www.acornrestaurant.co.uk

f @acornvegetarian
🐦 @acornvegetarian
📷 @acornrestaurant

Note in image 1:
2019
TRENCHERMAN'S
AWARDS
CREATIVITY
AND
INNOVATION

28 S A

Dan Moon at
The Gainsborough

Glamorous dining

Georgian architecture has been given a vibrant makeover in this three AA rosette restaurant at The Gainsborough Bath Spa hotel. The ambience is smart-informal, while menus range from great value lunches to indulgent five and seven course tasting menus. Admire the impressive wine wall while savouring chef Dan Moon's exquisite fine dining repertoire: locally sourced produce hits another level in pared-back, beautifully presented dishes.

Bath's thermal waters are piped right into the hotel, so it's worth making your visit an all-day affair and including a trip to the spa for a bliss-inducing treatment plus a two-course spa lunch or awesome afternoon tea.

Chef **Dan Moon**
3 course lunch from **£19**
3 course dinner from **£58**
Seats **68**
Bedrooms **99**
Room rate from **£290**

The Gainsborough Bath Spa, Beau Street, Bath, BA1 1QY
01225 358888
www.thegainsboroughbathspa.co.uk

f @thegainsboroughbathspa
🐦 @gainsbathspa
📷 @thegainsboroughbathspa

29

Mint Room – Bath

Bath's Indian jewel

Expect the vivacious flavours of traditional Indian cuisine with a shot of contemporary flair at this atmospheric restaurant which is all leather banquettes, dark wood and sparkling bronze.

British meat, seafood, veg and pulses are expertly conjured into artfully sophisticated plates. Discover a smattering of traditional curries on the menu, alongside new finds to intrigue such as Bengali spiced and smoked Creedy Carver duck breast, finished on the plancha and served with a creamy celeriac and cashew sauce.

The rooftop terrace, with its sweeping city views, is the perfect spot in which to indulge in champagne, cocktails and smaller dishes.

Chef **Soyful Alom**
3 course lunch from **£22.95**
3 course dinner from **£25**
Seats **80**

Longmead Gospel Hall, Lower Bristol Road, Bath, BA2 3EB
01225 446656
www.mintroom.co.uk

f @mintrooms
🐦 @themintroom
📷 @themintroom

Menu Gordon Jones

Off-piste eating

Picky eaters needn't bother joining the waiting list for a table at this innovative Bath eatery as chef patron Gordon Jones enjoys nothing better than surprising and delighting guests with eclectic combinations and off-piste ingredients.

The top-secret tasting menus (six courses at lunch, seven at dinner) are dictated by the restaurant's league of local suppliers and revealed to diners as each plate reaches the table. Inspiration comes from the ambitious chef's childhood in Scotland: *'Money was tight and everyone ate vegetables and cooked from scratch. It wasn't until I started writing menus that I realised how much of an influence my mother had been.'*

Chef **Gordon Jones**
6 course lunch **£55**
7 course dinner **£60**
Seats **22**

2 Wellsway, Bath, BA2 3AQ
01225 480871
www.menugordonjones.co.uk

🐦 @menugordonjones
📷 @menugordonjones

Elly Wentworth

The Angel – Taste of Devon (Nº72)

'Later this year I'll be visiting The Bath Priory (Nº**25**) – Michael Nizzero's cooking is skilful and creative.'

Somerset

Somerset

Restaurants listed in the guide correspond to the numbers plotted on the map.

 Full member

Standard member

31 Goodfellows

32 The Queens Arms

33 Little Barwick House

34 The Lord Poulett Arms

35 Augustus

36 The Rising Sun

37 The Globe, Milverton

38 The Luttrell Arms Hotel

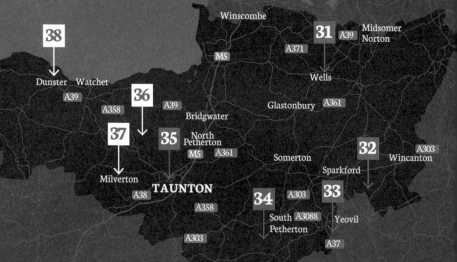

38

Dunster   Watchet

A39

A358

36

A39

Bridgwater

31   A39   Midsomer Norton

Winscombe

A371

M5

Wells

Glastonbury   A361

37

35

North Petherton

M5   A361

Somerton

Sparkford

32   A303   Wincanton

Milverton

A38

TAUNTON

A358

A303

34   A303

South Petherton   A3088

33

Yeovil

A37

All locations are approximate

31 S
Goodfellows
Established foodie find

Adam Fellows adds a dash of continental cuisine to the market town of Wells via his Mediterranean-inspired menus.

Seafood is the star of the show, and sparkling fillets of seabass with tapenade, and cod brandade spiked with chorizo take front and centre on a line-up which shifts by the season. The best way to explore the latest catch is in the dedicated seafood tasting menu.

Carnivores and vegetarians aren't left out in the cold either. An à la carte bill of delights such as potato and leek gnocchi with wild mushroom and chive sauce prove there are many strings to Goodfellows' bow.

Chef **Adam Fellows**
3 course lunch from **£27**
3 course dinner from **£35**
Seats **50**

5 Sadler Street, Wells, Somerset, BA5 2RR
01749 673866
www.goodfellowswells.co.uk

f @goodfellowseat
🐦 @goodfellowseat

32 S
The Queens Arms
Measuring food in metres, not miles

Tucked into the dramatic hills of the Somerset and Dorset border, this chic pub is a real gem.

A tempting stack of pork pies crowning the bar, and pumps loaded with local ales and ciders, signal to weary travellers that they've stumbled upon something rather special.

The family-run and quintessentially English Georgian inn attracts foodie pilgrims as a result of its good cooking and philosophy of measuring produce in metres, not miles. Nearby farms and the pub's own smallholding supply head chef Max and brigade with a wealth of seasonal ingredients.

Chef **Max Richfield**
3 course lunch from **£32**
3 course dinner from **£36.50**
Seats **78**
Bedrooms **8**
Room rate from **£85**

Corton Denham, Sherborne, Somerset, DT9 4LR
01963 220317
www.thequeensarms.co.uk

f @thequeensarmspub
🐦 @queensarmspub
📷 @queensarmspub

Little Barwick House
Rural foodie retreat

Set in tranquil gardens, this handsome Georgian dower house has long been a go-to for foodies in the know. Owned and run for the past 19 years by Tim and Emma Ford, the rural restaurant with rooms has held three AA rosettes since opening, as a result of the exquisite dining.

The menu is a tour de force of regional fare, including delicacies such as Forde Abbey's ruby red beef, Dorset Blue Vinney and Cornish fish and shellfish, which is complemented by an extensive and award winning wine selection.

It's open Tuesday to Saturday and you can extend your visit by staying in one of the charming and spacious guest rooms.

Chef **Tim Ford**
3 course lunch from **£28.95**
3 course dinner from **£31.95**
Seats **40**
Bedrooms **7**
Room rate from **£126**

Rexes Hollow Lane, Barwick, Yeovil, Somerset, BA22 9TD
01935 423902
www.littlebarwick.co.uk

f @littlebarwickhouse
🐦 @littlebarwick
📷 @littlebarwickhouse

Ross Sloan
Mount Haven Hotel and Restaurant (№129)

'I'm looking forward to visiting The Shore Restaurant (№**133**), Kota (№**128**) and The Idle Rocks (№**120**) this year.

'Brucie at The Shore Restaurant is a great friend and I have huge respect for the one-man-band of a chef.

'Jude is another good friend and I love his pan-Asian flavours.

'I've already visited The Idle Rocks this year but I'm looking forward to Guy cooking for me again soon.'

Take 5
GIN-STRONOMIC GREATS
Where edible adventures meet true-craft gins

Boringdon Hall

The creative presentation of the premium gins at this historic manor house is rivalled only by the inventive cooking of its head chef Scott Paton.

The Bell Inn

Dare to make a dent in the 90-strong list at this mother of all South West gin haunts and cosy destination dining pub.

Paschoe House

Any bar which displays a huge stuffed ostrich over the fireplace is pretty notable. Explore the 19-strong gin list before dinner.

The Old Quay House Hotel

Start your gastronomic adventure out on the waterside terrace, with a gin selected from a menu of 17.

The Painswick

Sink into a ginormous fireside sofa at this chic Gloucestershire hotel and work your way through the collection of 13 gins.

34 🅂
The Lord Poulett Arms
Dining pub discovery

Located in the picture-perfect hamstone village of Hinton St George, this popular inn has served as a rest stop for discerning travellers since 1680.

With thatched roof, bare stone walls and antique-style decor, it retains old-world charm while serving up a knockout seasonal menu that delivers on the promise of excellent dining pub fare. Feast on classics such as dayboat fish and chips and expertly aged local rump steak.

The courtyard garden, with its box hedges and pretty planting, makes an excellent spot for an alfresco aperitif. Upstairs, six stylish bedrooms await.

35

Augustus
Somerset stalwart

The best of seasonal British produce and French culinary flair collide at Richard Guest's neighbourhood bistro. Tucked away in a courtyard just off Taunton's main drag, the unassuming restaurant is a treasured secret among Somerset's resident foodies.

À la carte dishes cover the classics - think game pâté, rack of lamb with anna potatoes, and apple tarte tatin - while a couple of contemporary numbers, often with Asian influences, provide alternative thrills for more intrepid palates.

Sunday lunches at Augustus are rather special and tables fill quickly - booking is advised.

Chef **Philip Verden**
3 course lunch from **£26**
3 course dinner from **£26**
Seats **50**
Bedrooms **6**
Room rate from **£85**

High Street, Hinton St George, Somerset, TA17 8SE
01460 73149
www.lordpoulettarms.com

f @lordpoulettarms
@ @lord_poulett

Chef **Richard Guest**
3 course lunch from **£25**
3 course dinner from **£25**
Seats **40**

3 The Courtyard, St James Street, Taunton, Somerset, TA1 1JR
01823 324354
www.augustustaunton.co.uk

f @augustustaunton
@augustustaunton

Somerset

36

The Rising Sun

Stationed at the bottom of the Quantock Hills, this 16th century inn has provided hostelry, comforting home-cooked food and fine ales for weary ramblers for almost 450 years.

While its low-slung ceilings, dark wood beams and exposed brick walls hint at its heritage, The Rising Sun's contemporary menus prove it's certainly not stuck in the past.

Most of the ingredients are sourced from within five miles and beef used in the 28-day-aged steaks (cooked on volcanic hot stone) comes from cattle that graze on nearby Exmoor.

Chef **Jade Shorney.** 3 course lunch from **£25.**
3 course dinner from **£28.** Seats **72.** Bedrooms **2.**
Room rate from **£95**

Stout Lane, West Bagborough, Taunton, TA4 3EF
01823 432575
www.therisingsunbagborough.co.uk

f @therisingsunwestbagborough
🐦 @risingsun_pub

37

The Globe, Milverton

Tired travellers will be thankful to have this crowd-pleasing pub - a short detour from the M5 near Taunton - in their little black book of just-off-the-motorway finds.

Healthy appetites are satiated by a hearty line-up of proudly homemade classics such as tempura tiger prawns, slow-roasted glazed pork belly, and shortcrust steak and kidney pie.

Chef patron Mark Tarry also chalks weekly specials on the board - inspired by the season and whatever local delights he can get his hands on.

Chef **Mark Tarry.** 3 course lunch from **£21.**
3 course dinner from **£23.** Seats **40.** Bedrooms **2.**
Room rate from **£65**

Fore Street, Milverton, Taunton, Somerset, TA4 1JX
01823 400534
www.theglobemilverton.co.uk

f @theglobemilverton
🐦 @infomilverton
📷 @theglobemilverton

38

The Luttrell Arms Hotel

Located in the medieval village of Dunster, on the edge of Exmoor National Park, this elegant hotel packs plenty of character. Period features, quirky decor, open fires and an enchanting garden with views of Dunster Castle make it a delightful find.

Under the direction of head chef Barrie Tucker, the hotel's fine dining restaurant, Psalter's, deals in creative cooking crafted from the likes of rose veal and Creedy Carver duck breast. If you're in the mood for more casual fare, the pub's menu offers hearty and informal feasting.

Chef **Barrie Tucker.** 3 course lunch from **£20.**
3 course dinner from **£30.** Seats **45.** Bedrooms **29.**
Room rate from **£120**

32-36 High Street, Dunster, Somerset, TA24 6SG
01643 821555
www.luttrellarms.co.uk

f @theluttrellarmshotel
🐦 @luttrellarms
📷 @luttrellarms

Dorset & Hampshire

Nº45
Brassica Restaurant

Dorset & Hampshire

Restaurants listed in the guide correspond to the numbers plotted on the map.

Full member

Standard member

39	The Three Lions
40	Captain's Club Hotel
41	Rick Stein, Sandbanks
42	Abbots Court
43	The Club House
44	The Ollerod
45	Brassica Restaurant
46	Alexandra Hotel & Restaurant
47	The Yew Tree
48	Chewton Glen Hotel & Spa
49	WestBeach Restaurant
50	The Museum Inn
51	The Fontmell
52	Plumber Manor
53	Seasons, The Eastbury Hotel
54	Acorn Inn
55	The Crab House Cafe
56	The Station Kitchen
57	HIX Oyster & Fish House

Sherborn

44

45

54

53

Evershot

A37

46

Beaminster

Lyme Regis

West Bay

A35

57

56

43 Weymouth

55

All locations are approximate

39 S
The Three Lions
Niche dining in the New Forest

A cosy bar with open log fire makes this dog-friendly inn a perfect haven after a hearty ramble. Serving British/French classics crafted with precision and flair for over 20 years, The Three Lions is much more than just a welcome pub stop and has hosted numerous prestigious guests, from TV regulars to royalty.

Chef patron Michael Womersley and team prepare dishes from expertly sourced local produce, including homemade salmon gravlax and pigeon breast with wild mushrooms. An extensive wine list showcases fine sips from around the world. Indulge – then stay over in one of the en-suite rooms or five-room villa.

Chef **Michael Womersley**
3 course lunch from **£25.50**
3 course dinner from **£29.50**
Seats **60**
Bedrooms **7**
Room rate from **£125**

Stuckton, Fordingbridge, Hampshire, SP6 2HF
01425 652489
www.thethreelionsrestaurant.co.uk

40 S
Captain's Club Hotel
Smart waterside dining

Beside the River Stour in the historic Dorset town of Christchurch lies this four star contemporary hotel. As the name suggests it's a nautical escape, and tranquil interiors and sleek floor-to-ceiling windows create a perfect spot from which to study birdlife and passing boats.

Enjoy an alfresco G&T on the riverside terrace before heading into the restaurant where, in tune with the subtle seafaring theme, a decent selection of fresh fish and seafood dishes jostle for attention with carnivore classics such as herb-crusted roast rump of lamb. There's also an all-day menu for informal light bites.

Chef **Andrew Gault**
3 course lunch from **£19.50**
3 course dinner from **£32**
Seats **70**
Bedrooms **29**
Room rate from **£159**

Wick Ferry, Christchurch, Dorset, BH23 1HU
01202 475111
www.captainsclubhotelcom

f @captainclub
🐦 @theofficialcch
📷 @captainsclubhotel

41
Rick Stein, Sandbanks
Harbourside chic

Rick Stein's outpost in affluent Sandbanks showcases a mainly seafood menu in a modern maritime setting. Enjoy casual daytime dishes such as moules marinière or a fabulously fresh fillet of plaice in the downstairs bar while watching chefs plate pristine fish and seafood.

Upstairs, in the main restaurant, Poole Harbour becomes a glittering seascape for evening guests feasting on Seafood Restaurant classics such as turbot hollandaise and fruits de mer. Steaks hit the spot for committed carnivores while veggies can enjoy a menu of plant-based dishes.

Chef **Pete Murt**
3 course lunch from **£26**
3 course dinner from **£31**
Seats **145**

10-14 Banks Road, Sandbanks, Poole, Dorset, BH13 7QB
01202 283000
www.rickstein.com

f @ricksteinsandbanks
𝕏 @steinsandbanks
◎ @ricksteinrestaurants

42 S
Abbots Court
Field–to–fork dining

A walled kitchen garden, flock of chickens and rabble of pigs keep this Winterborne retreat expertly stocked with wonderfully fresh produce. The restaurant with rooms' field-to-fork philosophy, together with head chef Alex Naik's skill with inspired combinations and impressive plating, create a rustically refined dining experience which is rather special.

Seven beautifully boutique bedrooms make the opportunity to stay overnight tempting while one-of-a-kind pieces, a Farrow & Ball colour palette and roll-top tubs are downright Instagrammable.

Aspiring chefs and foragers will want to sign up for one of the seasonal workshops which include lunch and tailored tuition.

Chef **Alex Naik**
3 course dinner from **£40**
Seats **20**
Bedrooms **7**
Room rate from **£90**

East Street, Winterborne Kingston, Dorset, DT11 9BH
01929 448638
www.abbots-court.co.uk

f @abbotscourt
𝕏 @abbots_court
◎ @abbotscourt

Take 5

BEACHSIDE BEAUTIES

Revel in a dip and dine experience

Gylly Beach Cafe

As the sun sets over the stunning bay, ice creams and casual eating morph into smart sand-side dining.

Porthminster Beach Cafe

Asian-inspired dishes and Antipodean vibes call the shots at Porthminster's easy-going eatery.

The Dining Room at Saunton

Dine alfresco on Saunton Sands' terrace and swoon over good food and shimmering coastal scenery.

WestBeach Restaurant

Head to the spacious terrace to sample Dorset rock oysters, feast on steaming bowls of mussels and gaze over Poole Bay.

The Crab House Cafe

Plump Portland oysters (fresh from beds in the bay) are one of the many piscatorial pleasures to be savoured at this vibrant beach shack.

43
The Club House
Seafood and cocktail thrills

With its nautical New England vibe and spectacular sea views, this former Olympic-pool club house offers a setting straight out of a glossy interiors mag. The food (which, naturally, makes the most of the coastal location) is equally photogenic, so don't be shy about posting your supper on social.

Kick off an evening on the spacious deck with creative cocktails and a round of River Yealm oysters, before exploring a menu that makes seafood plucked from the Jurassic Coast the star of the show. The supporting cast of veggie sides and garnishes are sourced from the kitchen garden.

Chef **Charlie Soole**
3 course lunch from **£22**
3 course dinner from **£25**
Seats **60**

Beach Road, West Bexington, Dorchester, Dorset, DT2 9DG
01308 898302
www.theclubhousewestbexington.co.uk

f @theclubhousewestbexington
🐦 @theclubhouse217
📷 @theclubhouse2017

44 S
The Ollerod
A relaxed class act

The Ollerod (meaning cowslip in old Dorset dialect) is a beautifully quirky 13th century clergy house turned restaurant with rooms in historic Beaminster.

Chef proprietor Chris Staines held a Michelin star at London's Mandarin Oriental Hotel for nine years so you can rest assured you're in good hands as you explore the menu of seasonal modern British dishes crafted with veg from the walled kitchen garden.

Service is warm and unstuffy so guests also feel free to unwind with a cocktail, a glass of wine or a trad cream tea in the comfy bar and lounge, or out on the terrace.

Chef **Chris Staines**
3 course lunch from **£25**
3 course dinner from **£30**
Seats **40**
Bedrooms **13**
Room rate from **£130**

3 Prout Bridge, Beaminster, Dorset, DT8 3AY
01308 862200
www.theollerod.co.uk

f @theollerodbeaminster
🐦 @theollerod
📷 @theollerod

45

Brassica Restaurant

Eat (and shop) local

Brassica occupies a Grade II-listed building in Beaminster's town square and is owned and run by ex-Londoners Cass Titcombe and Louise Chidgey. The pair have created an environment to lift the spirits: bright and contemporary by day, softly candlelit by night.

Some 85 per cent of the (largely organic) menu is grown, caught or reared within a 15-mile radius of the restaurant and flavour-packed rustic dishes vibrate with Italian and Spanish influences.

Feast on delights such as hogget shoulder braised in chilli and served with polenta and pickles, then gently digest while perusing Brassica Mercantile's design-led homewares.

Chef **Cass Titcombe**
3 course lunch from **£20**
3 course dinner from **£30**
Seats **40**

4 The Square, Beaminster, Dorset, DT8 3AS
01308 538100
www.brassicarestaurant.co.uk

f @brassicarestaurant
🐦 @brassica_food
📷 @brassicarestaurant_mercantile

46 S

Alexandra Hotel & Restaurant

Seaside elegance

Positioned within skimming distance of Lyme Bay and the Cobb, this elegant seaside retreat enjoys some of the best views over Dorset's coastline. Originally built in 1735 as a family home, the Alexandra Hotel has tempted tourists to the Jurassic Coast for over a century and visitors continue to flock for their fill of sunshine and seafood.

The hotel's award winning restaurant is its pièce de résistance. Head chef Callum O'Doherty plucks inspiration from the ocean to craft crowd-pleasing dishes such as hot smoked Dorset mackerel with soba noodle salad. Carnivores and vegetarians will be equally pleased by locally-procured meat and veggie options.

Chef **Callum O'Doherty**
3 course lunch from **£31**
3 course dinner from **£38**
Seats **65**
Bedrooms **25**
Room rate from **£180**

Pound Street, Lyme Regis, Dorset, DT7 3HZ
01297 442010
www.hotelalexandra.co.uk

f @alexandrahotelandrestaurant
🐦 @alexandrahotel1
📷 @alexandrahotel_lymeregis

Dorset & Hampshire

47 S

The Yew Tree

This delightful 17th century pub with rooms, near Highclere Castle, offers eating options that range from snacks and small plates to mains and sharing dishes. Guests can even create their own bespoke tasting menu.

Relax beside a wood-burning fireplace with a local ale, or gather with the locals at the copper-top bar for a signature cocktail. Chef Matthew Sampson utilises fish from local rivers and game from nearby forests and, in summer, offers oysters on ice and lobster specials at an outdoor seafood bar.

Chef **Matthew Sampson.** 3 course lunch from **£25.** 3 course dinner from **£30.** Seats **75.** Bedrooms **8.** Room rate from **£80**

Hollington Cross, Andover Road, Highclere, near Newbury, Hampshire, RG20 9SE
01635 253360
www.theyewtree.co.uk

f @yewtreenews
🐦 @yewtreenews
📷 @theyewtreehighclere

48 S A

Chewton Glen Hotel & Spa

In its 130 acre setting on the edge of the New Forest (yet close to the beach) Chewton Glen is more than just a foodie destination.

Rock up at The Dining Room for modern British cooking fashioned from superb Hampshire ingredients and you'll be tempted to stay over in one of the romantic treehouses, visit the award winning spa, tennis centre and golf course, mosey around the heritage orchard and take a class in the James Martin Cookery School.

Chef **Luke Matthews.** 3 course lunch from **£32.** 3 course dinner from **£65.** Seats **180.** Bedrooms **72.** Room rate from **£325**

New Forest, Hampshire, BH25 6QS
01425 282212
www.chewtonglen.com

f @chewtonglenhotel
🐦 @chewtonglen
📷 @chewtonglen

49

WestBeach Restaurant

WestBeach throngs with foodies and staycationers who flock to its spacious terrace to sip cocktails, sample Dorset rock oysters and feast on steaming bowls of mussels while gazing over Poole Bay.

Even when the weather turns and winter creeps in, the casual spot remains popular thanks to its chic interiors and friendly atmosphere. While locally caught fish and seafood headline on head chef Matt Cook's daily menu, innovative vegetarian dishes and meatier options ensure there's a choice for everyone.

Chef **Matt Cook.** 3 course lunch from **£24.75.** 3 course dinner from **£29.25.** Seats **82**

Pier Approach, Bournemouth, Dorset, BH2 5AA
01202 587785
www.west-beach.co.uk

f @westbeach
🐦 @westbeachbmouth
📷 @westbeachbmouth

50 S

The Museum Inn

For a quintessentially British country inn experience, this Dorset dining destination oozes charm and character. Chef Neil Molyneux's experienced hand makes imaginative use of local game (in keeping with the pub's hunting traditions), along with other meat and fish. Head to the low-ceilinged, flagstone-floored bar for fireside wines and local ales, before settling down to an elegant dinner in The Shed.

The 17th century inn, which offers eight country-style bedrooms and a private cottage, is well positioned for exploring the Dorset countryside.

Chef **Neil Molyneux.** 3 course lunch from **£35.** 3 course dinner from **£35.** Seats **80.** Bedrooms **8.** Room rate from **£80**

Farnham, near Blandford Forum, Dorset, DT11 8DE
01725 516261
www.museuminn.co.uk

f @themuseuminnnews
📷 @themuseuminn

12 Abbots Court *

Escape to luscious Dorset countryside for exquisite dishes which parade the garden's choice pickings to beautiful effect.

14 The Bell

Modern British cooking reigns at this AA Hospitality Pub of the Year which, in addition to a kitchen garden, flaunts a brewery, distillery and smokehouse.

87 Lewtrenchard Manor

Feast in historic panelled dining rooms on produce plucked from the traditional walled kitchen garden.

32 The Queens Arms

This find on the Somerset and Dorset border deserves a visit for fine food crafted from goodies grown on its smallholding.

127 New Yard Restaurant

Relaxed and authentic dining in converted stables showcases veggies from the Trelowarren Estate.

51 S

The Fontmell

The babbling brook which flows between The Fontmell's bar and dining room is not the only unusual thing about it, as the quality of the cooking, its open fires, the cosy nooks and vintage wines, are also rather notable.

The menu utilises local game, meat (including Gloucester Old Spot/Berkshire pork bred nearby), fish and veg that's delivered daily to the kitchen door.

In summer, the garden is the place to be for top-notch G&Ts and stone-baked pizzas.

Chef **Tom Shaw**. 3 course lunch from **£19**.
3 course dinner from **£28**. Seats **40**. Bedrooms **6**.
Room rate from **£85**

Crown Hill, Fontmell Magna, Shaftesbury, Dorset, SP7 0PA
01747 811441
www.thefontmell.co.uk

f @thefontmell
🐦 @thefontmell
📷 @thefontmell

53 S

Seasons, The Eastbury Hotel

This listed former gentlemen's residence with walled gardens offers a delightful slice of Georgian glamour which can be enjoyed by visitors to its award winning restaurant.

While the hotel basks in history, its Seasons restaurant - led by executive chef Matthew Street - takes a contemporary approach. Classics are given a 21st century twist with the addition of intriguing flavours and innovative techniques. In summer, dine alfresco on the terrace and enjoy the delights of the idyllic setting.

Chef **Matthew Street.** 3 course lunch from **£30**.
3 course dinner from **£30**. Seats **45**. Bedrooms **21**.
Room rate from **£195**

Long Street, Sherborne, Dorset, DT9 3BY
01935 813131
www.theeastburyhotel.co.uk

f @theeastbury
🐦 @eastbury_hotel
📷 @theeastbury

52 S

Plumber Manor

Idyllic country houses often pass through a number of proprietors once they've been established as a luxury hotel, yet Plumber Manor is owned and run by the same family that built it in the early 1600s.

Opening their home and its 16 classic bedrooms to the public, owners Richard and Alison Prideaux-Brune excel in courteous service and welcome guests to this gorgeous Jacobean manor with pride. Dinner at the restaurant is a rather splendid affair which finishes in decadent fashion thanks to the famous dessert trolley. The lazy Sunday lunches are also rather special.

Chef **Louis Haskell**. 3 course lunch from **£33**.
3 course dinner from **£40**. Seats **65**. Bedrooms **16**.
Room rate from **£160**

Hazelbury Bryan Road, Sturminster Newton,
Dorset, DT10 2AF
01258 472507
www.plumbermanor.co.uk

54 S

Acorn Inn

This 16th century coaching inn, run by husband and wife Richard and Natalie Legg, is a hugely atmospheric spot for a pub lunch or dinner. It boasts old beams, oak panelling, crackling log fires, an original skittle alley and even a mention in *Tess of the d'Urbervilles*.

It's a cosy setting for chef Robert Ndungu's great cooking, while two bars (offering real ales, local ciders and whiskies galore), plus smart bedrooms, tempt visitors to linger longer.

Chef **Robert Ndungu.** 3 course lunch from **£25**.
3 course dinner from **£35**. Seats **50**. Bedrooms **10**.
Room rate from **£105**

28 Fore Street, Evershot, Dorchester, Dorset, DT2 0JW
01935 83228
www.acorn-inn.co.uk

f @acorninndorset
🐦 @acorn_inn
📷 @acorn_inn

55

The Crab House Cafe

Plump Portland oysters (fresh from beds in the bay) are one of the many piscatorial pleasures to be savoured at this vibrant beach shack. Head chef Will Smith tweaks the menu twice-daily, depending on what the Portland and Weymouth dayboats haul in.

In summer, there's a carefree, almost Caribbean vibe as you sit beneath blush pink umbrellas and drink in glorious views while feasting on stir-fried crab. In stormy weather, it's prudent to be inside for a wine-matched dinner of dishes such as baked saddle of monkfish with yellow split peas, bacon and spiced aubergine caviar.

Chef **Will Smith.** 3 course lunch from **£31.** 3 course dinner from **£31.** Seats **40**

Ferrymans Way, Portland Road, Wyke Regis, Dorset, DT4 9YU
01305 788867
www.crabhousecafe.co.uk

f @crabhousecafe
@ @thecrabhousecafe

56

The Station Kitchen

A historic railway carriage on the tracks of a former station isn't the first place you'd look for fresh-from-the-ocean fish and locally-shot venison, but The Station Kitchen's one-of-a-kind setting secures it a spot on your must-visit list.

Head to the platform cocktail bar for a pre-dinner pep-up before boarding the train for first class feasting. Fusion fare from chef patron Claire Moore plays with the classics - think wholegrain ham hock croquettes, salt and pepper buffalo wings and chorizo scotch egg with chipotle mayo.

Chef **Claire Moore.** 3 course lunch from **£29.** 3 course dinner from **£31.** Seats **55**

Station Road, West Bay, Bridport, Dorset, DT6 4EW
01308 422845
www.station.kitchen

f @thestationkitchen
@stationwestbay
@ @thestationkitchen

57

HIX Oyster & Fish House

Phenomenally fresh seafood does the talking at Mark Hix's Lyme Regis restaurant.

Watch the setting sun through floor-to-ceiling windows while devouring the local catch or, on sunny days, nibble scrumpy-fried rock oysters and Bigbury Bay cockle popcorn on the terrace.

The menu varies according to the daily fishing boats' bounty, but delicious staples include fresh fish on-the-bone and monkfish curry. Keep an eye open for Mark's Kitchen Table - an intimate dining experience in the chef's Dorset home.

Chef **Jeremy Bird.** 3 course lunch from **£23.50.** 3 course dinner from **£23.50.** Seats **45**

Cobb Road, Lyme Regis, Dorset, DT7 3JP
01297 446910
www.hixoysterandfishhouse.co.uk

f @hixoysterandfishhouse
@hixrestaurants
@ @hixrestaurants

Devon

Devon

Restaurants listed in the guide correspond to the numbers
plotted on the map.

 Full member

 Standard member

58	The Farmers Arms
59	Number Eight
60	The Dining Room at Saunton
61	Watersmeet Hotel
62	The Coach House by Michael Caines
63	The Masons Arms Knowstone
64	The Swan
65	The Riviera Hotel and Restaurant
66	Saveur
67	Lympstone Manor
68	The Galley Restaurant
69	The Salutation Inn
70	The Lamb at Longdown
71	The NoBody Inn
72	The Angel - Taste of Devon
73	Twenty_Seven by Jamie Rogers
74	Soar Mill Cove Hotel
75	Glazebrook House Hotel
76	Boringdon Hall
77	Barbican Kitchen
78	The Greedy Goose
79	Rock Salt Cafe
80	Paschoe House
81	Gidleigh Park
82	Two Bridges Hotel
83	The Cornish Arms
84	The Horn of Plenty
85	Hotel Endsleigh
86	The Arundell Arms Hotel & Restaurant
87	Lewtrenchard Manor
88	Pyne Arms
89	Peter Mundy at The Ginger Peanut
90	The Rock Inn
91	The Royal George
92	Highbullen Hotel Golf and Country Club
93	The Rams Head Inn and Country Hotel
94	The Lamb Inn at Sandford
95	Rodean Restaurant
96	Mill End Hotel
97	The Horse
98	Ilsington Country House Hotel and Spa
99	The Old Library Restaurant
100	The Royal Seven Stars
101	The Royal Castle Hotel
102	Gara Rock
103	Salcombe Harbour Hotel & Spa
104	The Fig Tree @ 36

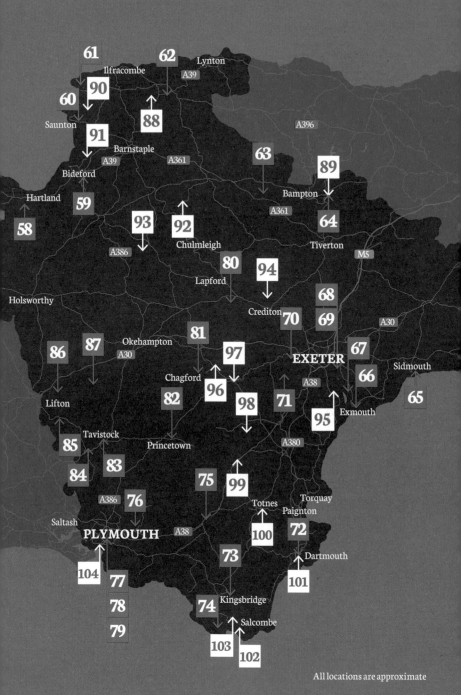

All locations are approximate

58
The Farmers Arms
New rural retreat

The future of Woolsery's thatched village inn looked bleak until tech entrepreneur Michael Birch - whose grandmother grew up in the north Devon village - acquired the keys in 2015. Three years (and huge investment) later, The Farmers Arms has been transformed into a stylish dining destination of note.

Prop up the gorgeous dark wood bar and graze on artisan snacks such as homemade pork scratchings with bramley apple ketchup. Alternatively, pick a table (by one of the four open fireplaces) in the restaurant and feast on ingredient-driven dishes crafted by premium-pedigree exec chef Ian Webber.

Chef **Ian Webber**
3 course lunch from **£21.50**
3 course dinner from **£35**
Seats **58**

Woolsery, Bideford, Devon, EX39 5QS
01237 439328
www.woolsery.com

f @farmersarmswoolsery
@farmersarmswoolsery

59
Number Eight
New gourmet go-to

After a few years working in Cornish restaurants, Joshua Jones and Chloe Wilks decided to spread their wings and express their passion for great food and service in their own establishment. The result is a delightful dining experience in the small north Devon town of Bideford.

The setting may be simple and unassuming, but the cultured cooking and warm service is bang on the money. Joshua works alone in the kitchen, crafting sophisticated and seasonal modern British food, while Chloe manages front of house with aplomb.

Chef **Joshua Jones**
3 course dinner from **£42**
Seats **20**

8a Allhalland Street, Bideford, Devon, EX39 2JD
01237 237589
www.numbereightrestaurant.com

f @Number Eight Restaurant
@08numbereight
@numbereightrestaurant

60 S
The Dining Room at Saunton
Art Deco dining by the sea

Visitors to Saunton Sands Hotel are increasingly being thoroughly spoilt when it comes to the gourmet element of their seaside getaway.

Recent head chef Mathias Oberg continues to go from strength to strength with his brigade (last year achieving a second AA rosette for the hotel) and has created a smart and elegant experience in the Art Deco Dining Room. Other developments include the implementation of a wellbeing menu to pair with the hotel's new uber-luxe Source spa.

In summer, be sure to book a table out on the terrace for world-class views of miles of shimmering coastline.

Chef **Mathias Oberg**
3 course Sunday lunch from **£30**
3 course dinner from **£40**
Seats **150**
Bedrooms **83**
Room rate from **£158**

Saunton, near Braunton, Devon, EX33 1LQ
01271 890212
www.sauntonsands.co.uk

f @sauntonsandshotel
🐦 @sauntonsandshot
📷 @saunton_sandshotel_devon

61 S
Watersmeet Hotel
Culinary coastal chic

A beach-lovers paradise – and recent winner of the Condé Nast Johansens Best Waterside Hotel – this boutique retreat enjoys glorious sea views and private steps down to Combesgate Beach. Inside, New England-style decor provides a chic and restful ambience that extends from the well-appointed rooms to the Pavilion restaurant.

Through a regularly changing menu, head chef John Prince dazzles diners with his skilful cooking. Dishes such as smoked pigeon and sirloin of Exmoor beef with crisp ox tongue can be savoured while enjoying uninterrupted coastal vistas.

The restaurant (and a more informal bistro) are open to non-residents, while hotel guests can also use the indoor and outdoor pools and spa facilities.

Chef **John Prince**
3 course lunch from **£26**
3 course dinner from **£50**
Seats **45**
Bedrooms **27**
Room rate from **£130**

Woolacombe, Devon, EX34 7EB
01271 870333
www.watersmeethotel.co.uk

f @watersmeethotel1
🐦 @watersmeethotel
📷 @watersmeetwoolacombe

The Coach House
by Michael Caines

Contemporary cuisine
in the countryside

This Michael Caines restaurant, in the rural splendour of boutique hotel Kentisbury Grange, lures foodies onto Exmoor for exceptional cuisine, contemporary decor and a well stocked bar.

Head chef James Checkley and team skilfully deliver Caines' innovative yet classical cooking style in beautifully presented dishes. The menu is a thoughtful representation of seasonal produce, offering delicacies such as roe deer and sole boudin.

For an indulgent culinary escape, plump for a gourmet weekend experience and sample the extensive tasting menu, three-course à la carte offering and luxury accommodation.

Chef **James Checkley**
3 course lunch from **£28.95**
3 course dinner from **£50**
Seats **54**
Bedrooms **22**
Room rate from **£180**

Kentisbury Grange Hotel,
Kentisbury, Barnstaple,
Devon, EX31 4NL
01271 882295
www.kentisburygrange.com

f @kentisburygrange
🐦 @kentisburyg
📷 @kentisburygrange

63

The Masons Arms Knowstone

Moorside Michelin star

A cosy welcome is guaranteed at this 13th century thatched inn - whether you're popping in for a pint of real ale in the rural bar or heading through to the simple but elegant dining room for award winning cooking.

Chef proprietor Mark Dodson and team, which includes wife Sarah who runs front of house, were awarded a Michelin star just six months after opening. They've retained the accolade for over a decade and Mark's first book, *This Is Mine*, was published in 2017.

Visit for local seasonal produce such as terrine of rabbit and loin of venison, served with verdant views of Exmoor.

Chef **Mark Dodson**
3 course lunch from **£27.50**
3 course dinner from **£45**
Seats **28**

Knowstone, South Molton, Devon, EX36 4RY
01398 341231
www.masonsarmsdevon.co.uk

f @Masons Arms Knowstone
🐦 @masonsknowstone
📷 @masonsarms_kitchen

64 S A

The Swan

Pub dining par excellence

This two-time winner of Trencherman's Best Dining Pub boasts a trophy cabinet full of awards - the result of Paul and Donna Berry's relentless pursuit of excellence at their village inn.

A classic dining pub menu balances quality with value, and the results can be tasted in favourites such as Exmoor lamb shank, and steak and kidney suet pudding.

The friendly rustic venue attracts destination diners while also keeping loyal locals well fed and watered, so booking in advance is advised. To explore the top-notch drinks menu in full, treat yourself to an overnight stay in one of the three smart bedrooms.

Chefs **Paul and Donna Berry**
3 course lunch from **£25**
3 course dinner from **£30**
Seats **60**
Bedrooms **3**
Room rate from **£90**

Station Road, Bampton, Tiverton, Devon, EX16 9NG
01398 332248
www.theswan.co

f @The Swan
🐦 @theswanbampton
📷 @theswanbampton

65 Ⓢ

The Riviera Hotel and Restaurant

A cut above

This imposing establishment on Sidmouth's esplanade offers charming English seaside views and smart two AA rosette dining.

Attention to detail is the defining characteristic of chef Martin Osedo's modern British menus, while the hotel's heritage adds traditional appeal. Not only has The Riviera been run by the Wharton family for over four decades, the seafood on its menu is supplied by a third-generation local fishing family.

Get into the glamorous spirit of the place by sipping a cocktail in the Regency Bar or pose at lunch on the sunny terrace.

Chef **Martin Osedo**
2 course lunch from **£27**
3 course dinner from **£42**
Seats **80 restaurant, 60 terrace**
Bedrooms **26**
Room rate from **£214**

The Esplanade, Sidmouth, Devon, EX10 8AY
01395 515201
www.hotelriviera.co.uk

66

Saveur

Exmouth excellence

After training under acclaimed chef Michael Womersley, Nigel Wright headed off to travel the world with partner Kerry Dutton before the duo took over Saveur in Exmouth in 2017.

Their culinary escapades influence everything at the charming neighbourhood restaurant and the pared-back daily menu and relaxed bistro vibe clearly reference continental dining culture.

The seafood offering at this coastal restaurant is impeccably fresh and the daily catch served with cockle tartare butter and the season's pick of vegetables.

Chef **Nigel Wright**
3 course lunch from **£19.50**
3 course dinner from **£35**
Seats **30**

9 Tower Street, Exmouth, Devon, EX8 1NT
01395 269459
www.saveursrestaurant.com

f @lessaveursrestexeter
@ @saveurexmouth

67 S

Lympstone Manor

Michelin-starred glamour

It's been a stellar year for Lympstone Manor, which recently won Best for a Blast of Sea Air in the Condé Nast Gold List and jumped 34 places to the number 20 spot in *Harden's Best UK Restaurants*.

Chef proprietor Michael Caines' vision of unparalleled country house hospitality is borne out in sumptuous accommodation and Michelin star-winning cuisine. Sample exceptional dishes in one of three unique dining rooms which offer views of the Exe Estuary.

Recently, Michael's passion for wine has extended beyond the creation of a world-class cellar to the planting of 17,500 vines in Lympstone's new 10.5-acre vineyard.

Chef **Michael Caines**
3 course lunch from **£48**
3 course dinner from **£135**
Seats **60**
Bedrooms **21**
Room rate from **£280**

Courtlands Lane, Exmouth, Devon, EX8 3NZ
01395 202040
www.lympstonemanor.co.uk

f @lympstonemanor
🐦 @lympstone_manor
📷 @lympstone_manor

68

The Galley Restaurant

Intimate elegance

The short but sweet menu at this bijou restaurant reads like an ode to the British coastline. Fish and shellfish – mostly sourced from Brixham and Fowey – take centre stage on the five-dish bill, with support from locally-shot game and Devon-grown veggies.

New head chef Jason Mead took the reins at the end of 2018 and has done an impressive job of upholding the restaurant's good reputation in waterside Topsham. The wine list, which features some fine Devon sparklers and a good selection by the glass, calls for a visit by train, taxi – or boat.

Chef **Jason Mead**
3 course lunch from **£22**
3 course dinner from **£28**
Seats **48**

41 Fore Street, Topsham, Exeter, Devon, EX3 0HU
01392 876078
www.galleyrestaurant.co.uk

f @thegalleytopsham
🐦 @galleytopsham
📷 @galleytopsham

69 S
The Salutation Inn
Topsham jewel

The estuary town of Topsham is blessed with a bounty of foodie destinations and at its heart lies one of the jewels in its culinary crown: The Salutation Inn.

Since taking over the business half a decade ago, Tom and Amelia Williams-Hawkes have earned the 18th century restaurant with rooms an enviable reputation for Tom's British/French fusion food, first class service and an exceedingly good wine list.

Not to be missed are the GlassHouse seasonal dinners, where lucky guests feast on hyper-local suppers under starry skies.

Chef **Tom Williams-Hawkes**
3 course lunch from **£26.50**
4 course dinner from **£45**
Seats **28**
Bedrooms **6**
Room rate from **£135**

68 Fore Street, Topsham, Exeter, Devon, EX3 0HL
01392 873060
www.salutationtopsham.co.uk

f @salutationtopsham
🐦 @salutation1
📷 @salutationinn

70
The Lamb at Longdown
The great escape

As you sip your aperitif in front of the fire at this rural dining pub you'll find it difficult to believe you're less than a ten minute drive from busy Exeter.

Local chef Dolton Lodge (formerly of The Galley in Topsham) took over the inn at the start of 2018 and has brought a formal – but unfussy – style of cooking to the former village boozer. Upgraded pub favourites share menu space with intricate and well executed à la carte dishes, with everything crafted from local ingredients and plated with camera-ready precision.

Chef **Dolton Lodge**
3 course lunch from **£19**
3 course dinner from **£24**
Seats **28**

Longdown, Exeter, Devon, EX6 7SR
01392 811100
www.thelamblongdown.co.uk

f @thelamblongdown
🐦 @thelamblongdown
📷 @thelamb_longdown

71 [S]
The NoBody Inn
Whisky galore in Devon

Only eight miles from Exeter, this 17th century country pub - all blackened beams and rustic antiques - feels like it's a world away from the city. There's a lovely garden and quirky bedrooms, but the choice of over 250 whiskies is its real claim to fame, winning the pub Trencherman's Best Bar List 2017.

The menu showcases seasonal local ingredients, from River Teign mussels to Creedy Carver duck. Discerning sippers will also appreciate the extensive wine list (which features over 30 available by the glass) and orange-spiked house gin.

Chef **Michael Pooley**
3 course lunch from **£24**
3 course dinner from **£30**
Seats **50**
Bedrooms **5**
Room rate from **£79**

Doddiscombsleigh, Exeter, Devon, EX6 7PS
01647 252394
www.nobodyinn.co.uk

f @thenobodyinn
🐦 @thenobodyinn
📷 @thenobodyinn

72
The Angel
– Taste of Devon
New wings at The Angel

Expansive views of the harbour, a thoroughbred fine dining heritage and a former *MasterChef: The Professionals* runner-up at the helm - there are plenty of good reasons to visit The Angel.

Fresh from Lucknam Park, rising culinary star Elly Wentworth heads up the kitchen and oversees a regularly changing menu that takes its lead from bountiful seasonal produce. Expect locally sourced and foraged ingredients such as roast diver-scallops and Dartmoor lamb.

The smart dining space has an exclusive but relaxed ambience and includes a discreet open-plan kitchen that'll delight curious home cooks.

Chef **Elly Wentworth**
3 course lunch from **£29.95**
3 course dinner from **£45**
Seats **45**

2 South Embankment, Dartmouth, Devon, TQ6 9BH
01803 833488
www.theangeldartmouth.co.uk

f @theangeltasteofdevon
🐦 @theangeldevon
📷 @theangeltasteofdevon

73 [S]

Twenty_Seven by Jamie Rogers

New for 2019

After learning his craft under some of the region's finest chefs, the South West Chef of the Year winner launched his solo venture at the end of 2018 - creating quite a buzz in Kingsbridge and beyond.

Creativity pulses through this young chef's kitchen and his six and eight course tasting menus are an adventure in flavour, texture and colour.

The local South Hams larder is raided for unique and seasonal ingredients, which are then cleverly coerced into dishes to delight. Even the drinks pairings are unusual: discover contemporary couplings such as fillet of Dexter beef and Spanish lager, and chocolate and olive oil delice with Venezuelan rum.

Chef **Jamie Rogers**
3 course lunch from **£30**
3 course dinner from **£40**
Seats **40**

9 Mill Street, Kingsbridge, Devon, TQ7 1ED
01548 288847
www.jamierogerschef.com

f @twentysevenbyjamierogers
🐦 @twenty_seven_x
📷 @twenty_seven_x

74 [S]

Soar Mill Cove Hotel

Gourmet holiday hotspot

Planning a family getaway and want to take the dog too? You should bookmark this well-appointed hotel in the hills above salubrious Salcombe as it offers flexible family rooms, three self-catering properties and secluded couples' suites, as well as a spa with spring-fed indoor pool. And dogs are welcome too.

Enswathed in an Area of Outstanding Natural Beauty, Soar Mill Cove is well placed for exploring the South Hams or working up an appetite along the South West Coast Path. Chef Ian MacDonald keeps guests well fed with his fine dining menu of superior meat and seafood from the rolling pastures and pristine shores nearby.

Chef **Ian MacDonald**
3 course lunch from **£30**
3 course dinner from **£39**
Seats **60**
Bedrooms **22**
Room rate from **£199**

Malborough, Kingsbridge, Devon, TQ7 3DS
01548 561566
www.soarmillcove.co.uk

f @soarmillcovehotel
🐦 @soarmillcove
📷 @soarmillcovehotel

Glazebrook House Hotel

Surprise and delight

This luxuriously quirky hotel, which last year won the Trencherman's Best Dine and Stay Award, surprises and delights at every turn. Full of curiosities (there's a cigar and whisky room, a bust of the Queen and unusual adornments on every wall) it's a feast for *all* the senses.

Using ingredients sourced within a 50-mile radius, head chef Joshua Ackland and team create unique and considered dishes such as gin-rubbed guinea fowl and curried cauliflower fondant. The addition of a chef's table provides an exclusive dining experience that's close to the action.

After a day exploring the moors and an evening of gastronomic delight, nine distinctively decorated bedrooms beckon guests.

Chef **Joshua Ackland**
3 course lunch from **£20**
3 course dinner from **£35**
Seats **55**
Bedrooms **9**
Room rate from **£99**
South Brent, Plymouth, Devon, TQ10 9JE
01364 73322
www.glazebrookhouse.com

f @glazebrookhousehotel
🐦 @glazebrookhouse
📷 @glazebrookhouse

Boringdon Hall

A taste of history

Although only 20 minutes from central Plymouth, Boringdon Hall feels a world away from the city's bustle. Dramatic Elizabethan buildings provide historic grandeur while the contemporary Gaia Spa switches things up with uber-modern interiors and cutting edge treatments.

Since 2016, the three AA rosette Gallery Restaurant has been in the skilled hands of head chef Scott Paton whose commitment to seasonality and sourcing sings from every dish. Presentation is elegant, flavours immaculately balanced and two tasting menus – complemented by wine flights – relieve the torture of decision making.

Chef **Scott Paton**
3 course dinner from **£55**
Seats **54**
Bedrooms **42**
Room rate from **£120**

Boringdon Hill, Plymouth, Devon, PL7 4DP
01752344455
www.boringdonhall.co.uk

f @boringdonhall
🐦 @boringdonhall
📷 @boringdonhall

77
Barbican Kitchen
Distilled to perfection

Hats off to chefs Chris and James Tanner whose contemporary brasserie remains a crowd-pleasing hotspot more than a decade after its debut.

The Kitchen offers that winning combination of unique location (inside the historic building that also houses the Plymouth Gin Distillery), creative menu and modern decor. There's even a fabulous private dining room, providing a memorable venue for parties of up to 22.

Visit for seafood that's fresh off the Looe dayboats, and local meats sourced by Philip Warren Butchers which are slow cooked to melting perfection or chargrilled with ninja-style elan.

Chef **Martyn Compton**
3 course lunch from **£18.95**
3 course dinner from **£18.95**
Seats **100**

60 Southside Street, Plymouth Gin Distillery,
Plymouth, Devon, PL1 2LQ
01752 604448
www.barbicankitchen.com

f @barbicankitchen
𝕏 @barbicankitchen
◎ @barbicankitchen

78
The Greedy Goose
Historic house dining

The acclaimed Plymouth restaurant, run by brothers Ben and Jake Palmer, just happens to be located in the city's oldest building - Prysten House - which also has its own well, attractive courtyard and private dining space.

The Goose was awarded two AA rosettes just five weeks after opening and, five years on, the offering is just as good in dishes such as pared-back (but perfectly executed) smoked haddock scotch egg and malt glazed pork belly. For the full epicurean experience, try Tuesday's extensive tasting menu.

For a more informal and seafood-focused taste of what chef patron Ben can conjure, try his new venture, The Sardine Factory Restaurant, which opened in Looe last summer.

Chef **Ben Palmer**
3 course lunch from **£13**
3 course dinner from **£13**
Seats **50**

Prysten House, Finewell Street, Plymouth,
Devon, PL1 2AE
01752 252001
www.thegreedygoose.co.uk

f @greedygooseplym
𝕏 @greedygooseplym
◎ @greedygooseplym

Rock Salt Cafe

Rejoice in the choice

Award winning chef Dave Jenkins gives the season's luscious local produce an imaginative fusion makeover at his family-run brasserie in Plymouth.

He's also on a mission to let customers call the shots and has launched a new multi-menu approach which offers diners a mix of simple sharing dishes, formal three-course dinners and a full-on tasting experience.

Creative dishes include salt and vinegar doughnuts with caviar, cucumber and smoked mackerel; Devon beef buns with beef jus, garlic, mushrooms and cauliflower; and Chiang Mai pork belly with king prawns, papaya, peanuts, lime and crackling. Vegans get their own equally tantalising menu.

Chef **David Jenkins**
course lunch from **£18**
course dinner from **£27**
Seats **60**

1 Stonehouse Street, Plymouth, Devon, PL1 3PE
1752 225522
www.rocksaltcafe.co.uk

@rocksaltcafeuk
@rocksaltcafeuk
@rocksaltcafe

Paschoe House

Fresh country house experience

As you approach the Victorian splendour of Grade II-listed Paschoe House, twinkling lights from mullioned windows beckon you in to experience fireside armchairs and a cosy bar.

If feasting is your fancy, head to the dining room to experience the fine dining menus of new head chef Craig Davies, which are inspired by French and Asian cuisine.

By day, energetic visitors can stroll in the 25-acre grounds or strike out, dogs in tow, on the Two Moors Way to stimulate their appetite for a casual meal in the morning room or library bar.

Other luxuries include afternoon teas (including sneaky teapot cocktails) and tasting menus at both lunch and dinner.

Chef **Craig Davies**
5 course tasting lunch **£40**
Dinner from **£55**
Seats **20**
Bedrooms **9**
Room rate from **£189**

Bow, Crediton, Devon, EX17 6JT
01363 84244
www.paschoehouse.co.uk

f @paschoehouse
@paschoehouse
@paschoehouse

81 S

Gidleigh Park

Reputation for excellence

Set in 107 acres of tumbling streams, ancient woodland and moss-covered granite on the edge of Dartmoor, Gidleigh is as rooted in its special landscape as it is in the South West culinary scene.

It's long been a must-visit on every *Trencherman* reader's hit list and continues to live up to its reputation for stellar food, one of the best wine cellars in the UK and top-notch service.

Sit on the terrace and sip a glass of Champagne as you bathe in the sounds of the natural world. Then move into the oak-panelled dining room for classical cooking crafted with a vitality and beauty that echoes the bucolic surroundings.

Chef **Gareth Howarth**
3 course lunch from **£65**
3 course dinner from **£125**
Seats **50**
Bedrooms **24**
Room rate from **£275**

Chagford, Newton Abbot, Devon, TQ13 8HH
01647 432367
www.gidleigh.co.uk

f @gidleighpark
🐦 @gidleighhotel
📷 @brownswordhotels

82 S

Two Bridges Hotel

Great escape on Dartmoor

This busy foodie hotel and restaurant has long been a magnet for day-trippers and those seeking a romantic break in the heart of the ancient Dartmoor landscape (its rural setting means it's a perfect place to reconnect).

In winter, two roaring log fires and cosy antique-filled lounges make it a very desirable bolthole, while the hotel's location between two bridges and a tumbling Dartmoor stream creates an idyllic outdoor spot for a summer's day lunch or afternoon tea.

Talented chef Mike Palmer creates beautifully crafted fine dining dishes which are served in the oak-panelled dining room. Head to the bar for informal British classics.

Chef **Mike Palmer**
3 course lunch from **£22**
3 course dinner from **£49**
Seats **60**
Bedrooms **32**
Room rate from **£99**

Dartmoor National Park, Devon, PL20 6SW
01822 892300
www.twobridges.co.uk

f @twobridgeshotel
🐦 @two_bridges
📷 @two_bridges_hotel

Adam Banks
**Jamie Oliver's
Fifteen Cornwall (Nº114)**

'I've dined at Outlaw's
Fish Kitchen (Nº110)
and it was absolutely
delicious, so Restaurant
Nathan Outlaw (Nº109) is
definitely on my list.'

83 Ⓢ

The Cornish Arms
Friendly and fabulous

Chef proprietor John Hooker enjoys the
enviable reputation of being one of the most
smiley chefs in the business, so it's no surprise
that his Tavistock dining pub is loved for its
warm conviviality.

Just like the chef, the food is unpretentious,
but top quality. Classic combinations and
well-sourced ingredients have earned the
inn many accolades and it currently holds a
Michelin Bib Gourmand and sits at number
18 in the Top 50 Gastropubs list.

Dine in the restaurant, bar or beer garden or, if
going home is the last thing on your mind, roll
to bed in one of seven luxe guest rooms.

Chef **John Hooker**
3 course lunch from **£26**
3 course dinner from **£28**
Seats **50**
Bedrooms **7**
Room rate from **£85**

15-16 West Street, Tavistock, Devon, PL19 8AN
01822 612145
www.thecornisharmstavistock.co.uk

f @cornisharms
🐦 @cornisharmstavy
📷 @the_cornish_arms_tavistock

The Horn of Plenty

Edge–of–Dartmoor dining

For a special country house getaway, you'd be hard pressed to find a more idyllic location than this edge-of-Dartmoor hotel and restaurant.

Views from The Horn's handsome bedrooms take in a vast sweep of the Tamar Valley, evenings can be toasted with pre-dinner champagne in the drawing room, and meals finish with coffee and petits fours in a restaurant which has wowed guests for over half a century.

Head chef Ashley Wright has a deft touch when it comes to turning seasonal and local ingredients into dishes to delight. Plump for the tasting menu for the full Devon experience.

Hotel Endsleigh

Romantic Regency

This Grade I-listed Regency fishing lodge – a former residence of the Duke of Bedford – is owned and has been designed by the Polizzi hotelier family, so it's no surprise that it exudes an air of stylishly refined and restrained elegance.

Nineteen beautiful bedrooms, including six suites, are set in acres of romantic gardens (designed by Humphry Repton) which include rose-wreathed arches and lawns that sweep down to the River Tamar.

Diners can enjoy the ravishing original features of the wood panelled, crest-studded dining room as an atmospheric backdrop to menus that showcase the freshest Cornish catch and rural Devon delicacies.

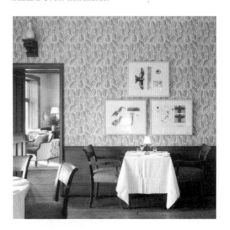

Chef **Ashley Wright**
3 course lunch from **£26**
3 course dinner from **£52.50**
Seats **64**
Bedrooms **16**
Room rate from **£130**

Milton Abbot, Tavistock, Devon, PL19 8JD
01822 832528
www.thehornofplenty.co.uk

@hornofplentyhotel
@hornofplenty1
@the_hornofplenty

Chef **Thomas Ewings**
3 course lunch from **£30**
3 course dinner from **£52.50**
Seats **40**
Bedrooms **19**
Room rate from **£200**

Milton Abbot, Tavistock, Devon, PL19 0PQ
01822 870000
www.hotelendsleigh.com

f @hotelendsleigh
🐦 @hotelendsleigh
📷 @hotelendsleigh

Take 5

PLANT-BASED PLEASURES

Vegan and veggie menus worth hunting out

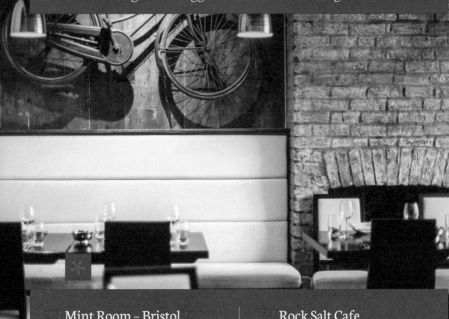

Mint Room - Bristol

No passport is required to take a veggie tour of the Indian subcontinent at Mint Room's Bristol outpost.

The Olive Tree Restaurant

Chris Cleghorn applies his exceptional skills to deliver exquisite vegetarian and vegan tasting menus at Bath's new Michelin starred venue.

Acorn Restaurant

A fresh and inventive take on vegan dining rewrites the rules on gourmet cooking sans-meat.

Rock Salt Cafe

Dave Jenkins' pan-global cooking also comes in vegan flavour. A tasting menu includes the likes of smoked and grilled watermelon, and jackfruit bao buns.

Lucknam Park Hotel & Spa

Hywel Jones' Michelin-starred skills are showcased in a stellar vegetarian tasting menu and vegan lunches at the country house hotel.

86 S

The Arundell Arms Hotel & Restaurant

Sporting seasonal delights

After a day spent at the hotel's fly fishing school, what could be more enjoyable than feasting on a sumptuous dinner in a glittering chandeliered dining room?

Whether you're relaxing after a day's sport in the wilds of Dartmoor, or simply dropping by for a culinary treat, there's indulgent luxury to be found here. Begin with a glass of bubbly or your pick from the burgeoning range of South West gins in the bar before dining on dishes crafted by new head chef Chris Heaver.

Go à la carte or plump for the five course seasonal tasting menu. And, thanks to comfortable country-themed bedrooms, there's every excuse to succumb to the hotel's charm and stay over.

Chef **Chris Heaver**
3 course lunch from **£23**
3 course dinner from **£38**
Seats **60**
Bedrooms **26**
Room rate from **£160**

Fore Street, Lifton, Devon, PL16 0AA
01566 784666
www.arundellarms.com

f @arundellarmshotel
🐦 @thearundellarms
📷 @arundellarmshotel

87 S

Lewtrenchard Manor

Jacobean splendour

This very special ancient house, with its wood-panelled dining rooms, historic portraits and crackling fires, makes a charming setting in which to experience the contemporary cooking of its new head chef, Tom Browning.

Start your evening by exploring the exceedingly good collection of wines by the glass in the elegant lounge, before heading into the dining room for a dinner crafted from interesting produce – some of it plucked straight from the walled kitchen garden.

For a thoroughly unusual eating experience, book The Purple Carrot private dining room which offers a unique view of the kitchen.

Chef **Tom Browning**
3 course lunch from **£25.50**
3 course dinner from **£49.50**
Seats **40**
Bedrooms **14**
Room rate from **£150**

Lewdown, Okehampton, Devon, EX20 4PN
01566 783222
www.lewtrenchard.co.uk

f @lewtrenchard
🐦 @lewtrenchard
📷 @lewtrenchardmanor

Devon

Pyne Arms

Ravishingly rural

Owners Ellis and Amie Pannell succeed in exceeding expectations at the Pyne Arms. A menu of hearty pub classics belies the passion and creativity that's been poured into every element of the rural Exmoor inn.

The pub hums with the chatter of happy locals, and pairs front of house friendliness with delicious and original takes on familiar dishes. Everything is crafted from local cuts and crops.

Eat in the bar or dining room and, in summer, the courtyard terrace is a perfect spot for alfresco feasting.

Don't want to go home after dinner? A night in one of the characterful bedrooms sets you up to explore the rolling Exmoor countryside on the pub's doorstep.

Chef **Ellis Pannell**
3 course lunch from **£17.50**
3 course dinner from **£28**
Seats **60**
Bedrooms **3**
Room rate from **£75**

East Down, Barnstaple,
Devon, EX31 4LX
01271 850055
www.pynearms.co.uk

f @thepynearms
🐦 @pynearms
📷 @pynearms

89 S

Peter Mundy at The Ginger Peanut

This intimate restaurant offers a smart take on out-of-town dining with a menu that befits its edge-of-Exmoor setting.

Atmospheric low lighting and plush plaid chairs will have you slowing down to savour chef proprietor Peter Mundy's dishes that are fashioned from local and seasonal produce. The prospect of five stylish bedrooms and a hearty breakfast will tempt you to further explore the local spirits, wines and beers on offer.

Chef **Peter Mundy.** 3 course lunch from **£20.**
3 course dinner from **£30.** Seats **50.** Bedrooms **5.**
Room rate from **£76.50**

19 Fore Street, Bampton, Tiverton, Devon, EX16 9ND
01398 332244
www.gingerpeanut.co.uk

f @thegingerpeanut
🐦 @thegingerpeanut
📷 @petermundyatthegingerpeanut

90

The Rock Inn

This 17th century pub is tucked away in the north Devon coastal village of Georgeham.

Foodies-in-the-know swing by on the way home from the beach for deli boards, curries and local lamb, venison, seafood and home-reared rare breed pork crafted into classic dining pub dishes. Scallops with black pudding, and Exmouth mussels are locals' faves.

The drinks list features five Cask Marque real ales, local ciders, a long wine list, many gins and Lyme Bay Winery's fizz by the glass. Eat by the fire in the cosy bar or out back in the airy conservatory.

Chef **Damon Owens.** 3 course lunch from **£15.**
3 course dinner from **£20.** Seats **80**

Rock Hill, Georgeham, Devon, EX33 1JW
01271 890322
www.therockinn.biz

f @rock.inn.96
📷 @therockinngeorgeham

91 S

The Royal George

With 180-degree views over the estuary, the best seats in the house at this waterside restaurant are beside the huge floor-to-ceiling windows. Making the most of the stunning location and bringing the area's natural beauty inside were top of the list when the historic pub was renovated in 2018.

The menu reflects the north Devon terroir and locally landed fish is a regular headliner on a line-up that shifts daily. Looking for somewhere to stay? Find four gorgeous guest rooms upstairs.

Chef **Greg Martin.** 3 course lunch from **£25.**
3 course dinner from **£30.** Seats **80.** Bedrooms **4.**
Room rate from **£90**

Irsha Street, Appledore, Devon, EX39 1RY
01237 424138
www.trgpub.co.uk

f @theroyalgeorgeappledore
🐦 @trg_appledore
📷 @trg_appledore

92 S

Highbullen Hotel Golf and Country Club

Driving up to the steep gabled roofs and dramatic stone archways of this Arts and Crafts manor house, one can't fail to be impressed. Destination dining is paired with lavish accommodation (especially the award winning Loft Suite), golf course, new Laura Ashley tea room and indulgent spa treatments.

Dinner in the Devon View Restaurant sees the local catch, crops and cuts served as smart dishes in elegant surrounds – with accompanying views of Exmoor.

Chef **Stephen Walker.** 3 course lunch from **£21.50.**
3 course dinner from **£39.** Seats **80.** Bedrooms **39.**
Room rate from **£139**

Chittlehamholt, Umberleigh, Devon, EX37 9HD
01769 540561
www.highbullen.co.uk

f @highbullenhotel
🐦 @highbullen
📷 @highbullen

93 S

The Rams Head Inn and Country Hotel

The residents of Dolton couldn't believe their luck when chef Nicolas Boucher and wife Vanessa took over their village pub in 2018. Michelin-trained Nico didn't waste any time in putting his mark on the rural inn, introducing a menu that combines Devon produce with French cooking.

In summer, enjoy a glass of white and a bowl of mussels in the courtyard garden; winter calls for a spot close to the wood-burner and pie of the day. There are eight en-suite bedrooms, too.

Chef **Nicolas Boucher.** 3 course lunch from **£18.** 3 course dinner from **£24.** Seats **50.** Bedrooms **8.** Room rate from **£80**

South Street, Dolton, Devon, EX19 8QS
01805 804255
www.theramsheadinn.co.uk

f @theramsheadinnatdolton
🐦 @theramsdolton
📷 @theramsatyourservice

94 S

The Lamb Inn at Sandford

Foodies up for navigating mid-Devon's warren of country lanes are rewarded with a top-notch supper and a remarkable choice of tipples at Sandford's village pub.

The lip-smackingly fresh produce that stocks the lunch and dinner menus doesn't have to travel far though, as landlord Nick Silk works with head chef Andy Bennett to source meat from the fields surrounding the 16th century inn.

Passing after a stomp with the dog? Bring your pooch in (they're welcome) and enjoy a moment's tranquility by the open fire with a local G&T and artisan ciabatta.

Chef **Andy Bennett.** 3 course lunch from **£18.50.** 3 course dinner from **£30.** Seats **39.** Bedrooms **7.** Room rate from **£75**

Sandford, Crediton, Devon, EX17 4LW
01363 773676
www.lambinnsandford.co.uk

f @lambinnsandford
🐦 @lambInnsandford
📷 @lambinnstagram

Bruce Rennie
The Shore Restaurant (Nº133)

'I'm really keen to try out New Yard Restaurant (Nº127) under chef Jeffrey Robinson.

'He has the same working ethos as me in regard to sustainability and local produce – and the food he's producing looks great.'

95

Rodean Restaurant

This family-run restaurant, not far from Powderham Castle, has recently been refurbished and received a contemporary new interior to match its menu of modern Mediterranean-inspired dishes.

Exploring Devon's coast and country on a quest for the county's best produce, chef patron Matthew Tilt gathers his finds on an explorative tasting menu and daily à la carte bill. Such is the popularity of the chef's dishes that the restaurant has recently opened for lunch on the weekend. Foodies with a nose for fine wines are encouraged to attend one of the regular pairing events.

Chef **Matthew Tilt.** 3 course lunch from **£28.** 3 course dinner from **£28.** Seats **38**

The Triangle, Kenton, Exeter, Devon, EX6 8LS
01626 890195
www.rodeanrestuarant.co.uk

f @rodeanrestaurant
🐦 @rodean_kenton
📷 @rodean_restaurant

96 S

Mill End Hotel

This country house hotel in its romantic setting beside the River Teign is just a few steps away from the wilds of Dartmoor, making it the perfect retreat after a day in your hiking boots.

Regather your strength with an elegant afternoon tea (with or without fizz) on the lawn or by the fire, before retreating to one of the country-style bedrooms to prepare for a fabulous dinner.

Come downstairs to expertly presented, classic British dishes like slow roasted pork belly stuffed with apricot and herbs - and be sure to leave room for the excellent cheeseboard.

Chef **Darren Knockton.** 3 course lunch from **£23.50.** 3 course dinner from **£37.** Seats **40.** Bedrooms **21.** Room rate from **£145**

Sandy Park, Chagford, Newton Abbot, Devon, TQ13 8JN
01647 432282
www.millendhotel.com

f @millendhotel
🐦 @millenddevon

97

The Horse

Mediterranean-style dishes are the surprise at this rustic dining pub in the heart of Dartmoor National Park.

Alongside hearty pub fare like chargrilled 21-day-hung steak, you'll find dishes such as pasta paccheri served with a rich ragout of slow-braised Tuscan sausages in red wine.

A tempting feast of pizzas from the custom-built oven is another of the draws for locals who also gather for Devon ales, the roaring fires and buzzing music nights.

Chef **Nigel Hoyle.** 3 course lunch from **£20.** 3 course dinner from **£25.** Seats **50**

7 George Street, Moretonhampstead, Devon, TQ13 8PG
01647 440242
www.thehorsedartmoor.co.uk

f @horsedartmoor
🐦 @horsedartmoor

98 S

Ilsington Country House Hotel and Spa

This hotel and award winning spa - set in ten acres, with Dartmoor on the doorstep - has been family-owned and run for over 20 years.

Chef Mike O'Donnell applies his culinary energy and interest in the moor's produce - both farmed and wild - to create modern menus. Lamb, beef and pork is born and bred on the moor and fish comes off dayboats at Brixham.

Complementing the main restaurant is a bistro, which provides sharing dishes of home-smoked and cured meat and fish.

Chef **Mike O'Donnell.** 3 course lunch from **£25.50.** 3 course dinner from **£41.** Seats **40.** Bedrooms **25.** Room rate from **£125**

Newton Abbot, Devon, TQ13 9RR
01364 661452
www.ilsington.co.uk

f @ilsingtonhotel
🐦 @ilsingtonhotel
📷 @ilsingtonhotel

Hywel Jones
Lucknam Park Hotel & Spa (Nº11)

'I hope to make it to Boringdon Hall (Nº**76**) in Plymouth this year. I've been lucky enough to cook with Scott Paton at a few events and his food has always been awesome.'

99

The Old Library Restaurant

From the warm-from-the-oven bread to the irresistibly crunchy honeycomb, every morsel to pass your lips at this heart-of-Dartmoor restaurant has been lovingly prepared by its trio of chefs.

After cutting their teeth at nearby Agaric Restaurant, founders Joe Suttie and Amy Mitchell launched the Ashburton eatery on North Street in 2016. Swing by early to enjoy a leisurely brunch, or make a dinner reservation and revel in seasonal cooking in pleasingly rustic surrounds.

Chefs **Amy Mitchell, Lewis Mitchell and Joe Suttie.** 3 course dinner from **£25.** Seats **24**

North Street, Ashburton, Devon, TQ13 7QH
01364 652896
www.theoldlibraryrestaurant.co.uk

f @theoldlibraryrestaurant
🐦 @theoldlibrary2
📷 @restaurantoldlibrary

100 S

The Royal Seven Stars

At the foot of Totnes' vibrant high street, this characterful coaching inn has provided a welcome stop for visitors since the 17th century. A traditional public house facade belies the modern interior, which includes deluxe rooms, a cocktail bar and the smart TQ9 restaurant.

Chef Martin O'Brien crafts contemporary dishes from seasonal ingredients (many of which are sourced from within a 20-mile radius of the hotel) such as locally landed fish of the day served with buttered samphire and River Exe mussels.

Chef **Martin O'Brien.** 3 course lunch from **£20.** 3 course dinner from **£20.** Seats **35.** Bedrooms **21.** Room rate from **£110**

The Plains, Totnes, Devon, TQ9 5DD
01803 862125
www.royalsevenstars.co.uk

f @royal7stars
🐦 @rsstotnes
📷 @royalsevenstarshotel

101 [S]

The Royal Castle Hotel

Residing over Dartmouth's waterfront for over 400 years, The Royal Castle is rich in maritime history. The popular hotel and restaurant honours this heritage with menus which swim with locally caught seafood such as Brixham crab and pan-fried turbot.

Downstairs, an oak-beamed bar hosts pub lunches and casual suppers of seafood chowder and homemade burgers, while The Grill Room restaurant offers more refined dishes such as saddle of lamb, rump steak and whole lemon sole.

2 course lunch from **£20.** 3 course dinner from **£30.** Seats **60.** Bedrooms **24.** Room rate from **£120**

11 The Quay, Dartmouth, Devon, TQ6 9PS
01803 833033
www.royalcastle.co.uk

f @royalcastlehotel
🐦 @rchdartmouth1
📷 @rch_dartmouth_

103 [S]

Salcombe Harbour Hotel & Spa

There are few dining destinations to rival Salcombe Harbour Hotel's location on the banks of the south Devon estuary. Request a window seat when you make your reservation at the Jetty Restaurant and dine to views of boats bobbing and kingfishers diving in the shimmering waters below.

As you'd expect from a chic coastal spot, head chef Jamie Gulliford's menu overflows with local seafood. For the complete Salcombe experience, order a chilled bottle of fizz and the fresh fruits de mer.

Chef **Jamie Gulliford.** 3 course lunch from **£24.95.** 3 course dinner from **£27.50.** Seats **93.** Bedrooms **50.** Room rate from **£195**

Cliff Road, Salcombe, South Hams, Devon, TQ8 8JH
01548 844444
www.harbourhotels.co.uk

f @salcombeharbourhotel
🐦 @salcombehhotel
📷 @salcombeharbourhotel

102 [S]

Gara Rock

The cross-country expedition to this clifftop hotel is a small taster of the sweeping rugged views which await in the restaurant's curved wall of floor-to-ceiling windows. It's worth pitching up (or booking) early to secure a ringside seat.

When the sun's shining, hikers, families and dog walkers gather the other side of the glass on the Gara terrace to feast on smoked mackerel, Salcombe crab sandwiches and giant burgers stuffed with blue cheese and crispy bacon. Come evening, more formal dining is the order of the day.

Chef **Chris Warrick.** 3 course lunch from **£26.** 3 course dinner from **£30.** Seats **100.** Bedrooms **29.** Room rate from **£250**

East Portlemouth, Salcombe, Devon, TQ8 8FA
01548 845946
www.gararock.com

f @gararockhotel
🐦 @gararock
📷 @gararockhotel

104

The Fig Tree @ 36

This family-run neighbourhood restaurant is the kind that everyone wishes was at the end of their street. So Plymouth's resident foodies were thrilled when The Fig Tree took over the former Samphire site at the end of 2017.

French bistro vibes create a rustic and relaxed setting while the front of house staff, led by co-owner Tanya Poole, are warmly welcoming. In the kitchen, chef patron Ryan Marsland specialises in unpretentious but delightful seasonal food.

Chef **Ryan Marsland.** 3 course lunch from **£23.** 3 course dinner from **£23.** Seats **40**

36 Admirality Street, Plymouth, Devon, PL1 3RU
01752 253247
www.thefigtreeat36.co.uk

f @thefigtreeat36
🐦 @figtreeat36
📷 @thefigtreeat36

Cornwall

Cornwall

Restaurants listed in the guide correspond to the numbers plotted on the map.

Full member

Standard member

105	The Springer Spaniel
106	Talland Bay Hotel
107	The Old Quay House Hotel
108	Carlyon Bay Hotel
109	Restaurant Nathan Outlaw
110	Outlaw's Fish Kitchen
111	The Seafood Restaurant
112	St Petroc's Bistro
113	Appleton's Bar & Restaurant
114	Jamie Oliver's Fifteen Cornwall
115	The Alverton
116	Tabb's Restaurant
117	The Lugger
118	The Nare
119	The Rosevine Hotel
120	The Idle Rocks
121	The Water's Edge at The Greenbank Hotel
122	Star & Garter
123	Oliver's
124	Rastella at Merchants Manor
125	Gylly Beach Cafe
126	The Royal Duchy Hotel
127	New Yard Restaurant
128	Kota
129	Mount Haven Hotel and Restaurant
130	BCK Bistro & Bottle Shop
131	Porthminster Beach Cafe
132	Harris's Restaurant
133	The Shore Restaurant
134	2 Fore Street Restaurant
135	The Sardine Factory Restaurant
136	The Nutty Duck at Trevalsa Court
137	The Dining Room
138	The Pickwick Inn & Oliver's Restaurant
139	The Old Mill House Bistro
140	Fistral Beach Hotel and Spa
141	Hooked! Restaurant & Bar
142	The Watch House
143	Brasserie on the Bay
144	Meudon Hotel
145	The Bay Hotel
146	The Square at Porthleven
147	The Bay at Hotel Penzance

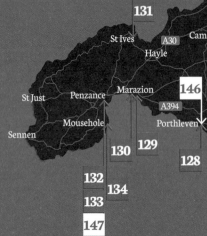

All locations are approximate

Ben Palmer

The Sardine Factory Restaurant (N°135) and The Greedy Goose (N°78)

'If I get a day off, I'd like to make a trip to Lewtrenchard Manor (N°87).

'Tom Browning is a good friend and an up-and-coming talent so I'm looking forward to trying his culinary delights.'

105 🅰

The Springer Spaniel

Foodies' best friend

Cornish tapas, creative tasting menus and a seasonal pop-up cocktail bar warrant a detour to this destination dining pub in the hamlet of Treburley.

Talented chef Connor Hawkings joined The Springer Spaniel family in February 2018 and brought with him a penchant for eye-catching plating and locally sourced ingredients.

Pub favourites such as handcrafted pies and Springer mac 'n' cheese share menu space with creative à la carte dishes so both young pups and stalwart springers will find something to get their tails wagging.

Chef **Connor Hawkings**
3 course lunch from **£25**
3 course dinner from **£30**
Seats **63**

Treburley, Launceston, Cornwall, PL15 9NS
01579 370424
www.thespringerspaniel.co.uk

f @thespringerspaniel
🐦 @springerthe
📷 @springerspanielpub

106 S
Talland Bay Hotel
Seafood at its source

Whether you're visiting for a light lunch, intimate dinner or blow-the-budget tasting menu experience, dishes at Talland Bay are designed to dazzle in both taste and presentation.

As befitting the country house hotel's rather beautiful position overlooking Porthallow Beach, chef Nick Hawke makes the most of sparklingly fresh Cornish seafood and fish. In summer, feast on grilled mackerel or crab salad on the terrace then, when the leaves fall, dine in the conservatory and enjoy the views from behind glass as you devour steaming bowls of Fowey mussels and choice Cornish cheeses.

Chef **Nick Hawke**
3 course lunch from **£25**
3 course dinner from **£49**
Seats **40**
Bedrooms **23**
Room rate from **£160**

Porthallow, Looe, Cornwall, PL13 2JB
01503 272667
www.tallandbayhotel.co.uk

f @tallandbayhotel
🐦 @tallandbayhotel
📷 @tallandbayhotel

107 S
The Old Quay House Hotel
Chic waterside dining

The well-heeled town of Fowey is chocka with chic shops, galleries, cafes and pubs, but there's nothing to quite rival the upmarket waterside dining experience of Quay House restaurant at The Old Quay House Hotel.

In summer, the only place to be seen is sipping a glass of Veuve Clicquot on the terrace of the boutique townhouse as boats clink in the harbour. A modern British menu gathers ingredients such as Fowey river mussels, local scallops, West Country beef and Cornish cheeses and serves them in style.

Chef **Richard Massey**
3 course lunch from **£32**
5 course dinner from **£45**
Seats **30**
Bedrooms **13**
Room rate from **£200**

28 Fore Street, Fowey, Cornwall, PL23 1AQ
01726 833302
www.theoldquayhouse.com

f @theoldquayhousehotel
🐦 @theoldquayhousehotel
📷 @oldquayhouse

108 S
Carlyon Bay Hotel
Art Deco glamour

Set within 250 acres of unspoilt grounds and with unparalleled views over St Austell Bay, Carylon Bay is the jewel in the crown of the family-run group of Brend Hotels.

With its 18-hole championship golf course, luxurious spa, outdoor pool and the South West Coast Path on its doorstep, there's plenty to keep guests occupied, although you may not find anything to eclipse head chef Paul Leakey's impressive cooking at the Bay View Restaurant. Delight in fine dining in Art Deco surrounds or, for a more relaxed experience, the Taste Brasserie showcases local produce in simpler dishes.

Chef **Paul Leakey**
3 course lunch from **£22.50**
3 course dinner from **£40**
Seats **150**
Bedrooms **86**
Room rate from **£150**

Sea Road, St Austell, Cornwall, PL25 3RD
01726 812304
www.carlyonbay.com

f @thecarlyonbayhotel
🐦 @carlyonbayhotel
📷 @carlyonbayhotel

109
Restaurant Nathan Outlaw
Seafood reigns supreme

With luscious coastal views and a menu dedicated to local seafood, Restaurant Nathan Outlaw demonstrates single-minded commitment to the treasures of the ocean. It's certainly a winning strategy, and one that's delivered two Michelin stars and the number one restaurant spot in *The Good Food Guide 2019*.

The set menu treats the sustainable catch from Cornish dayboats with Outlaw's renowned lightness of touch. Complement your courses with a smart wine flight or take a recommendation from the knowledgeable team.

Dinner is an intimate affair in the upstairs dining room or, if you fancy a spot of culinary voyeurism, book to eat in the kitchen bar and watch the chefs at work.

Chef **Nathan Outlaw**
3 course lunch from **£140**
3 course dinner from **£140**
Seats **30**

6 New Road, Port Isaac, Cornwall, PL29 3SB
01208 880896
www.nathan-outlaw.com

f @resnathanoutlaw
🐦 @resnathanoutlaw
📷 @resnathanoutlaw

110
Outlaw's Fish Kitchen
Quayside kitchen

Where better to enjoy Nathan Outlaw's seafood creations than in a 15th century fisherman's cottage on the harbourside at Port Isaac?

With just eight tables, this is a pretty unique dining experience where head chef Tim Barnes and team create small seafood plates from the day's catch (as much as possible coming from local inshore dayboats).

Dishes like crispy ling with pickled veg and smoked paprika mayonnaise let the essence of the main ingredient shine in an unfussy but oh-so-clever way.

Desserts such as chocolate, peanut and lime baked alaska are prepared with the same meticulous magic.

111 S
The Seafood Restaurant
Padstow pilgrimage

There are now 12 in the Stein family of restaurants, but The Seafood Restaurant is where Rick and Jill first conceived their winning formula of smart casual dining, ultra-fresh local seafood and interesting wines from across the globe.

Inspired by the TV series and cookery books, ardent fans make a pilgrimage to the jewel in the crown to experience Stein classics as created by The Seafood Restaurant's talented long-time head chef Stephane Delourme.

It's often busy but it is possible to rock up (sans reservation) and grab a stool at the bar where you can watch sashimi being prepared as you tuck in to lunch.

Chef **Stephane Delourme**
3 course lunch from **£42.95**
3 course dinner from **£45**
Seats **130**
Bedrooms **16** (and an additional 6 in St Edmund's House)
Room rate from **£165**

Riverside, Padstow, Cornwall, PL28 8BY
01841 532700
www.rickstein.com

f @theseafood
🐦 @theseafood
📷 @ricksteinrestaurants

Chef **Tim Barnes**
3 course lunch from **£50**
3 course dinner from **£50**
Seats **20**

1 Middle Street, Port Isaac, Cornwall, PL29 3RH
01208 881183
www.nathan-outlaw.com

f @outlawsfishkitchen
🐦 @fish_kitchen
📷 @fishkitchen

112 S
St Petroc's Bistro
Padstow's hidden gem

Rick and Jill Stein's rustic-chic gem is a laid-back, friendly place to eat good food and escape the summer crowds. Find foodie respite in the garden on sunny days or there's a private dining room if you're really craving time out from the harbourside bustle.

Chef Mark O'Hagan produces bistro classics with honed skill which are devised to show off top-notch produce such as 30-day dry-aged Hereford beef.

Start your visit with drinks in the lounge or next door at sister venue Ruby's Bar where the creative cocktail list includes a range inspired by members of the Stein clan (Rick's Ceylon Negroni is a must).

Chef **Mark O'Hagan**
3 course lunch from **£19.95**
3 course dinner from **£31**
Seats **50**
Bedrooms **10** (and an additional 4 in Prospect House)
Room rate from **£165**

4 New Street, Padstow, Cornwall, PL28 8EA
01841 532700
www.rickstein.com

f @stpetrocsbistro
🐦 @stpetrocsbistro
📷 @ricksteinrestaurants

113
Appleton's Bar & Restaurant
Cornish–Italian fusion

Enjoy fresh local produce with creative Italian inspiration at the solo venture of former Fifteen Cornwall head chef Andy Appleton and partner Lyndsey.

Set in a Cornish vineyard – more precisely the modern space above Trevibban Mill – the restaurant offers a daily changing, inspiring menu: anyone for lobster tortellini made with plankton pasta dough?

An equally novel bar list features vermouths and artisan Italian liqueurs and you can choose from Italian wines or the vineyard's own label. On sunny Sundays, catch some rays on the terrace and refuel with a brunch of fried chicken and waffles or steak and eggs.

Chef **Andy Appleton**
3 course lunch from **£30**
3 course dinner from **£30**
Seats **50-100**

Trevibban Mill Vineyard & Orchards, Dark Lane, near Padstow, Cornwall, PL27 7SE
01841 541355
www.appletonsatthevineyard.com

f @appletonsbarandrestaurant
🐦 @_appletons
📷 @_appletons

Jamie Oliver's Fifteen Cornwall

Contemporary Cornwall

For modern Mediterranean-style dining paired with jaw droppingly expansive beachy views, Jamie's Watergate Bay restaurant gets ten out of ten.

Head chef Adam Banks and team (many of whom are the famed young apprentices) hold firm to the founding ethos of crafting innovative seasonal dishes which are rooted in Italian cuisine.

The food's good, the vibe buzzy and all profits go to Fifteen's charity: Cornwall Food Foundation. What's not to like?

It's open for coffee, lunch and dinner and you can even visit just for cocktails - though good luck swerving the elegant antipasti plates as you sip your house negroni.

Chef **Adam Banks**
3 course lunch from **£35**
3 course dinner from **£35**
Seats **110**

On the beach, Watergate Bay, Cornwall, TR8 4AA
01637 861000
www.fifteencornwall.co.uk

f @fifteencornwall
🐦 @fifteencornwall
📷 @fifteencornwall

Andrew Kojima
Koj (Nº10)

'I head to Cornwall three or four times a year with my family - usually visiting the area around Portscatho and St Mawes - so I'm looking forward to eating on the harbour at The Idle Rocks (Nº**120**).

'I'd also like to try Jude's food at Kota (Nº**128**) if I can wangle it - it looks fabulous.'

115 S
The Alverton
Country life in the city

Spend an evening at this former convent and you'll soon forget you're in the centre of Truro. Located at the top of a steep hill and surrounded by mature gardens, the charming hotel offers tranquility and foodie thrills without the cross-country drive.

Its smart restaurant sees head chef Simon George exploring Cornwall's coast and countryside on a menu that showcases classic combinations alongside contemporary plating and modern execution. Cornish crab, local mackerel and fillet of beef are à la carte stalwarts - ask the knowledgeable bar team for their choice of pairings from the sophisticated drinks list.

Chef **Simon George**
3 course lunch from **£20**
3 course dinner from **£26**
Seats **70**
Bedrooms **51**
Room rate from **£99**

Tregolls Road, Truro, Cornwall, TR1 1ZQ
01872 276633
www.thealverton.co.uk

f @alvertonhotel
🐦 @alvertonhotel
📷 @thealvertonhotel

116
Tabb's Restaurant
Truro's mini gem

This bijou restaurant blends so seamlessly with its Kenwyn Street neighbours, you'd be forgiven for mistaking it for a terrace house. Discerning diners, however, know that behind the front door lies a word-of-mouth success story which has garnered a loyal following in the Cornish capital.

The two AA rosette restaurant offers a dining experience so intimate and personal - it's just chef owner Nigel Tabb in the kitchen - that it feels like you're having supper in someone's home. The cooking showcases Nigel's passion for superb local produce and prowess for fashioning everything from freshly baked bread to homemade chocolates with consummate skill.

Chef **Nigel Tabb**
3 course lunch from **£27.50**
3 course dinner from **£27.50**
Seats **28**

85 Kenwyn Street, Truro, Cornwall, TR1 3BZ
01872 262110
www.tabbs.co.uk

f @tabbsrestaurant
🐦 @tabbsrestaurant

The Lugger

Slipway to heaven

Surrounded by the windswept headlands of the Roseland Peninsula, this 17th century smugglers inn is not short on Daphne Du Maurier-style charm.

Step inside its old-world exterior, though, and you'll discover why it's Cornwall's only five AA star inn: a smart two AA rosette restaurant and 24 coastal-chic bedrooms add more than a touch of luxury.

Head chef Richard Lipscombe creates dishes crafted from Cornish produce and seafood hauled from the harbour by the village's resident fishing vessels. Imbibe charming seascape views while tucking into local fish, lobster, crab and game.

Chef **Richard Lipscombe**
3 course lunch from **£20**
3 course dinner from **£37.50**
Seats **46**
Bedrooms **23**
Room rate from **£165**

Portloe, Truro, Cornwall, TR2 5RD
01872 501322
www.luggerhotel.co.uk

f @theluggerhotel
🐦 @theluggerhotel
📷 @thelugger29

The Nare

Push the boat out

In addition to panoramic sea views beyond colourful gardens and Carne Beach, this charming destination hotel also enjoys a rather special culinary offering.

The light-filled Quarterdeck restaurant has a lively, yachty vibe, while for elegant evening dining there's The Nare Dining Room with silver service and a five course table d'hôte menu crafted from the likes of locally hauled lobster and stunning Cornish beef.

Soak up the timeless atmosphere with a cocktail in the bar or an Admiral's Afternoon Tea on the terrace, or push the boat out and treat yourself to a stay in a comfortable bedroom and a day on the hotel's motor launch (with seafood picnic).

Chef **Brett Camborne-Paynter**
3 course lunch from **£25**
3 course dinner from **£40**
Seats **60**
Bedrooms **37**
Room rate from **£299**

Carne Beach, Veryan-in-Roseland, Cornwall, TR2 5PF
01872 501111
www.narehotel.co.uk

f @thenarehotel
🐦 @thenarehotel
📷 @thenarehotel

The Rosevine Hotel

Family feasting

Family friendly hotels aren't the first place you'd look for fresh-from-the-boat lobster or locally shot wood pigeon, yet bending the rules is all part of the fun at this coastal retreat. The Rosevine's modern interior was designed with families in mind and parents can delight in dropping future-foodies at the playroom and then heading off for a decadent dinner in the restaurant.

The hotel's relaxed Cornish vibe also makes it the perfect place to host friends for the weekend. The private dining room was recently named as one of the best in the country and head chef George Richards' seafood filled menus fuel the fun in style.

Chef **George Richards**
3 course lunch from **£18**
3 course dinner from **£26**
Seats **40**
Bedrooms **16**
Room rate from **£98**

Roseland, Portscatho, Cornwall, TR2 5EW
01872 580206
www.rosevine.co.uk

f @therosevine
🐦 @therosevine
📷 @therosevinecornwall

Tom Williams-Hawkes

The Salutation Inn (Nº69)

'I'm planning a visit to Bath to see what Dan Moon is cooking at The Gainsborough Bath Spa (Nº28), as well as visiting Chris Cleghorn at The Olive Tree Restaurant (Nº26).'

The Idle Rocks

Chic and sustainable

Sustainability and local produce may be buzzwords these days, but they hold great sway at this rather special hotel where head chef Guy Owen and team can identify where every ingredient comes from.

Menus are a celebration of the surrounding Roseland Peninsula and make the most of this champion produce in artfully simple yet creative dishes. A recent collaboration with the Lost Gardens of Heligan has brought in heritage veg from the Victorian walled gardens, grown especially for the Idle kitchen.

The dining areas - inside surrounded by owner Karen Richards' chic seaside styling, or out on the waterside terrace - are cool and sophisticated, completing the circle at the coveted dining destination.

Chef **Guy Owen**
3 course lunch from **£35**
3 course dinner from **£60**
Seats **60**
Bedrooms **19**
Room rate from **£200**

Harbourside, St Mawes,
Cornwall, TR2 5AN
01326 270270
www.idlerocks.com

f @theidlerocks
🐦 @theidlerocks
📷 @idlerocks

121 **S**

The Water's Edge
at The Greenbank Hotel

Harbourside haven

Nick Hodges' use of local lobster, Falmouth-landed fish and freshly picked seasonal vegetables at this waterside dining spot reveal the executive chef's loyalty to his Cornish heritage.

The all-day menu reads like a catalogue of the county's finest producers and features relaxed grazing plates and seafood platters alongside smart à la carte dinner dishes.

Kick off an evening at the chic hotel with a Trencherman's Award-winning cocktail in the beautiful circular bar before heading to the dining room with its panoramic views of Falmouth's deep blue harbour. Arriving by boat? Moor up at one of the hotel's private pontoons.

Chef **Nick Hodges**
3 course lunch from **£20**
3 course dinner from **£28**
Seats **90**
Bedrooms **61**
Room rate from **£109**

Harbourside, Falmouth,
Cornwall, TR11 2SR
01326 312440
www.greenbank-hotel.co.uk

f @greenbankhotel
🐦 @greenbankhotel
📷 @greenbankhotel

122 S A
Star & Garter

This historic pub overlooking Falmouth harbour offers robust, on-trend dining with cool decor to match. Chef Robert Bunny focuses on lesser-used cuts of locally reared meats (courtesy of the kitchen's own butchery room), freshly landed fish and traditional smoking, curing and preserving skills.

Expect bold flavours (as in pickled sardines with cucumber relish and treacle bread) on a daily changing menu which includes sharing platters. Even the celebrated Sunday roasts showcase Robert's inventive nose-to-tail approach.

Another highlight is the sweeping marine view - best enjoyed from the leather booths in the dining room or, if you're staying overnight, any of the three design-led apartments upstairs.

Chef **Robert Bunny**
3 course lunch from **£18**
3 course dinner from **£26**
Seats **40**
Bedrooms **4**
Room rate from **£90**

52 High Street, Falmouth, Cornwall, TR11 2AF
01326 316663
www.starandgarterfalmouth.co.uk

f @starandgarterfalmouth
🐦 @starfalmouth
📷 @starandgarterfalmouth

123 A
Oliver's

While Falmouth's holidaymakers have plenty of culinary greats to choose from, Ken and Wendy Symons' unassuming High Street bistro remains one of the most popular with both locals and tourists.

Seasonal meat, fish and vegetables are king at Oliver's, and a legion of West Country suppliers compete to stock Ken's busy kitchen with the freshest produce, which the small team then skilfully manipulate into palate-pleasing delights.

Oliver's status as a Cornish stalwart was cemented when it was named Best Restaurant in the 2018 Food Reader Awards.

Chef **Ken Symons**
3 course lunch from **£23**
3 course dinner from **£32**
Seats **28**

33 High Street, Falmouth, Cornwall, TR11 2AD
01326 218138
www.oliversfalmouth.com

🐦 @oliversfalmouth

124 S

Rastella at Merchants Manor

Ingredient—led dining

Only the very best locally sourced and seasonal produce makes the cut in Hylton Espey's kitchen. Rastella's chef patron puts Cornish ingredients in the spotlight and has even created a menu map, so guests can discover exactly where every item is sourced.

Produce procured, each dish is built around a focus on flavour, and smoking, searing and roasting in a wood-fired oven all add signature flair.

Those looking to stay over will find a collection of boutique bedrooms within the century-old manor house.

Chef **Hylton Espey**
3 course lunch from **£25**
3 course dinner from **£35**
Seats **64**
Bedrooms **39**
Room rate from **£130**

Western Terrace, Falmouth, Cornwall, TR11 4QJ
01326 312734
www.merchantsmanor.com

f @merchantsmanor
🐦 @mmerchantsmanor
📷 @rastellarestaurant

125

Gylly Beach Cafe

Chic eating at the beach

This award winning family-run cafe restaurant enjoys a prime spot on the sands of Falmouth's famous Gyllyngvase Beach, a setting diners get to enjoy as a result of the floor-to-ceiling windows and terrace.

By day, the cafe buzzes with a beachy, laid-back vibe, but as the sun sets the ambience turns more relaxed-formal and head chef Dale McIntosh's menus transition accordingly. Unfussy yet beautifully prepared cuisine is the order of the evening - think pan-seared seabass with Cornish scallops or roasted rump of West Country lamb. Creative and sometimes quirky dishes feature too.

Chef **Dale McIntosh**
3 course lunch from **£16**
3 course dinner from **£25**
Seats **65**

Cliff Road, Falmouth, Cornwall, TR11 4PA
01326 318740
www.gyllybeach.com

f @gyllybeachcafe
🐦 @gyllybeachcafe
📷 @gyllybeachcafe

126
The Royal Duchy Hotel
Classic Cornish hospitality

There are few better places to watch the sun slip into the turquoise waters of the Atlantic than from The Royal Duchy's spacious terrace. The grand seaside hotel has resided on Cornwall's coastline for over a hundred years, providing fabulous food and comfortable slumber for Falmouth's flurry of visitors.

At The Pendennis Restaurant, classic British fare is infused with flavours from Asia and the Mediterranean. A carefully curated evening menu often features favourites from land and sea such as poussin, venison and hake. There's also a children's menu for aspiring foodies.

Chef **John Mijatovic**
3 course lunch from **£22**
3 course dinner from **£39**
Seats **120**
Bedrooms **45**
Room rate from **£88**

Cliff Road, Falmouth, Cornwall, TR11 4NX
01326 313042
www.royalduchy.co.uk

f @theroyalduchyhotel
🐦 @brendroyalduchy
📷 @royalduchyhotel

127
New Yard Restaurant
Authentic eating on a country estate

Every effort is made to ensure the New Yard dining experience is as authentic as possible: bread and pasta is made twice daily in the busy kitchens, veggies are picked from the Trelowarren Estate walled garden or sourced from local producers and the menu devised to represent Cornwall throughout the seasons.

Dine in the cosy setting of the old stables or outside in the sheltered yard and get stuck in to an à la carte menu which changes daily. Come evening, hit the tasting menu to sample a wide range of dishes in one setting.

Chef **Jeffrey Robinson**
3 course lunch from **£29**
3 course dinner from **£38**
Seats **35**

Trelowarren Estate, Mawgan, Cornwall, TR12 6AF
01326 221595
www.newyardrestaurant.co.uk

f @trelowarrennewyard
🐦 @newyard
📷 @newyardrestaurant

2019
TRENCHERMAN'S
AWARDS
BEST CHEF

Kota

Award–winning fusion food

It seems there was hardly an accolade going last year that this charming harbourside restaurant didn't pick up, including three AA rosettes (for the first time) and a Michelin Bib Gourmand for the fifth year running. And now chef patron Jude Kereama has bagged Trencherman's Best Chef.

Expect a highly personalised menu, thanks to Jude's signature Asian twist, which is derived from his half Maori, half Chinese Malay heritage.

His outstanding level of culinary excellence is balanced by a joyful appreciation of good food and hospitality - an ethos supported by wife Jane who leads the front of house team.

An excellent-value tasting menu includes adventurous delights like hand-dived scallops with crispy belly pork, cauliflower, miso puree and soy apple dressing.

Porthleven is a beautiful spot that's well worth exploring and happily Kota also houses two four AA star rooms so you can dine and stay.

Chef **Jude Kereama**
3 course dinner from **£28**
7 course tasting menu **£60**
Seats **40**
Bedrooms **2**
Room rate from **£90**

Harbour Head, Porthleven,
Cornwall, TR13 9JA
01326 562407
www.kotarestaurant.co.uk

f @kotarestaurant
🐦 @kotarestaurant
📷 @kotarestaurant

Mount Haven Hotel and Restaurant

Nature's dining room

Adventurous, modern and inspired by nature' is now head chef Ross Sloan describes his style of cooking at Mount Haven.

The menus are sprinkled with unusual ingredients, foraged by the head chef along this stretch of rugged Cornish coastline. Dishes such as crab with avocado gazpacho and apple jelly are as picturesque as the stunning views of St Michael's Mount.

In summer, you'd be hard pressed to find a better natural dining room in Cornwall than the sunny terrace with its panoramic views of the shimmering bay.

Chef **Ross Sloan**
3 course lunch from **£26**
3 course dinner from **£33.50**
Seats **57**
Bedrooms **20**
Room rate from **£100**

Turnpike Road, Marazion, Cornwall, TR17 0DQ
01736 719937
www.mounthaven.co.uk

f @mounthavenhotel
🐦 @mounthavenhotel
📷 @mounthavenhotel

BCK Bistro & Bottle Shop

New wave wine pairings

After spending the winter vineyard-hopping across South Africa, grape enthusiast and talented chef Ben Prior decided to let wine take the lead at his Marazion bistro.

While the menu has always offered a pairing for each plate, the fresh set-up also welcomes a bottle shop to the family restaurant and allows patrons to pick their favourites to drink in or take home.

A concise bill of dishes designed to complement the fine vintages is updated daily depending on what (mostly Cornish) produce Ben can get his hands on. Influence is plucked from Asia, the Middle East and beyond; expect inventive compilations such as tandoori monkfish with fennel and kohlrabi.

Chef **Ben Prior**
3 course lunch from **£24**
3 course dinner from **£35**
Seats **32**

Marazion, Penzance, Cornwall, TR17 0EL
01736 719200
www.benscornishkitchen.com

f @Ben's Cornish Kitchen
🐦 @cornishkitchen
📷 @cornishkitchen

Take 5

DOG-FRIENDLY DELIGHTS

Well-behaved pooches welcome ...

The Horn of Plenty

Dogs can stay with their owners in a number of designated bedrooms and are also welcome for an aperitif in the library.

Lords of the Manor Hotel

Well-behaved pooches are welcome to stay in a number of bedrooms at this effortlessly glamorous country house hotel.

Soar Mill Cove Hotel

Take a yomp along the South West Coast Path to work up an appetite for a dinner of locally-sourced delights.

Talland Bay Hotel

Enjoy runs with Rover on Porthallow Beach and stay in one of the dog-friendly rooms. Dogs can dine with their faithful companion in the brasserie, though not in the fine dining restaurant.

The Three Lions

Experienced cooking, a seriously good wine list and a cosy bar with crackling log fire make this dog-friendly inn a haven after a rural ramble.

131
Porthminster Beach Cafe

Antipodean Asian thrills

The Beach Cafe's strikingly white Art Deco building, which sits right on the shore, is a siren luring foodies for Antipodean-style sand-between-the-toes dining.

In the midst of the Cornish winter you'll want to grab a table inside the whitewashed dining room, but if the weather's dry you'd be mad to eat anywhere but outdoors on the heated terrace.

The cooking capitalises on fabulous local seafood and is cleanly modern with an Asian theme. Pair carefully crafted dishes with a few picks from the stonking drinks list which includes an incredible 27 wines by the glass.

Chef **Michael Smith**
3 course lunch from **£30**
3 course dinner from **£30**
Seats **110**

St Ives, Cornwall, TR26 2EB
1736 795352
www.porthminstercafe.co.uk

@porthbcafe
@porthbcafe
@porthminstercafe

132
Harris's Restaurant

In it for the long haul

This boutique restaurant, which has appeared in the *Michelin Guide* since 1974, continues to be a delightful destination for discerning diners.

Chef Roger Harris's à la carte menus are fashioned around local bounty such as lamb and fillet steak as well as seasonal pleasures like venison and pheasant. Beautifully cooked fish and seafood (including whole Cornish lobster) are sourced daily from Newlyn fish market.

Those agonising between two or three courses take note: desserts such as iced lemon soufflé, encased in thin dark chocolate with fresh fruit sauce, are pretty irresistible.

Chef **Roger Harris**
3 course lunch from **£27.50**
3 course dinner from **£38**
Seats **20**

46 New Street, Penzance, Cornwall, TR18 2LZ
0101736 364408
www.harrissrestaurant.co.uk

Nº**113**
Appleton's Bar & Restaurant

133 🅰
The Shore Restaurant
First-class seafood

There's been a buzz about this tiny restaurant since it opened in Penzance in 2015. Chef owner Bruce Rennie made a name for himself in Edinburgh and Northern Ireland where he captained Michelin starred kitchens, so it wasn't a huge surprise when his first solo venture soon got the nod as one of the best fish restaurants in the country.

The daily bill of seven or eight tasting dishes is dictated by the local dayboats' catch and, for the full Shore experience, the matched wines are a must. For truly special occasions, there's a small private dining room which hosts up to four guests.

Chef **Bruce Rennie**
Tasting menu from **£58**
Seats **24**

13-14 Alverton Street, Penzance, Cornwall, TR18 2QP
01736 362444
www.theshorerestaurant.co.uk

f @theshorerestaurantpz
🐦 @the_shore_pz
📷 @the_shore_pz

134
2 Fore Street Restaurant
Harbourside hideaway

This bright and airy bistro on the harbour at Mousehole enjoys views across the village to Mount's Bay, making it a fabulous spot for laid-back lunches and sensational suppers (especially in summer when you can enjoy the views).

Head chef Joe Wardell (classically trained under Raymond Blanc) and team serve a menu showcasing regional delicacies - from freshly landed seafood to local organic meat.

You can also dine alfresco in the secluded garden and stay the night in one of two chic boltholes.

Chef **Joe Wardell**
3 course lunch from **£30**
3 course dinner from **£34**
Seats **36**

Mousehole, Penzance, Cornwall, TR19 6PF
01736 731164
www.2forestreet.co.uk

135

The Sardine Factory Restaurant

A shoal of metal fish suspended from the ceiling that magically "swims" in the breeze is just one of the cheerful touches at this new harbourside restaurant in the fishing village of Looe.

Chef patron Ben Palmer has returned to his Cornish roots to offer pristine piscatorial dining in a relaxed family-friendly environment.

Sustainable seafood is picked each day from the market opposite and fashioned into strikingly fresh dishes, matched by quirky versions of classic desserts.

Chef **Ben Palmer.** 3 course lunch from **£15.** 3 course dinner from **£15.** Seats **75**

The Quay, West Looe, Cornwall, PL13 2BX
01503 770262
www.thesardinefactorylooe.com

f @thesardinefactorylooe
@ @thesardinefactorylooe

---

136 S

The Nutty Duck at Trevalsa Court

Set within Trevalsa Court, the newly named Nutty Duck is open for breakfast, lunch, afternoon tea and dinner. A clifftop position affords spectacular panoramic views across Mevagissey Bay - best enjoyed on sunny days from the terrace.

Chef Adam Cawood serves up fresh and unfussy food prepared with an abundance of sustainable and traceable provincial produce, which secured the restaurant two AA rosettes in 2016. Feast on locally landed fish, as well as Cornish meats and cheeses.

Chef **Adam Cawood.** 3 course lunch from **£15.** 3 course dinner from **£30.** Seats **28.** Bedrooms **14.** Room rate from **£100**

Trevalsa Court, Mevagissey, Cornwall, PL26 6TH
01726 842468
www.trevalsa-hotel.co.uk

f @trevalsacourt
🐦 @trevalsacourt
@ @trevalsacourt

Cornwall

137

The Dining Room

This upscale restaurant in the affluent holiday haunt of Rock specialises in classical cuisine which is thoughtfully crafted from the season's most luscious local produce.

It may attract the crowds in summer but, as a result of being open all year (evenings only), it's also built a local following for its reassuringly restrained menus. Visit for treats such as cider-cured mackerel fillet with pickled cucumber, apple, dill and saffron and an extensive wine list. Everything is homemade – right down to the clotted cream butter.

Chef **Fred Beedles**. 3 course dinner from **£48.** Seats **30**

Pavilion Buildings, Rock Road, Rock, Cornwall, PL27 6JS
01208 862622
www.thediningroomrock.co.uk

f @thediningrmrock
🐦 @thediningrmrock
📷 @thediningroomrock

138 S

The Pickwick Inn & Oliver's Restaurant

This lively and informal restaurant enjoys inspiring views over rolling hills to the Camel Estuary where you can just about spot the oyster beds that supply the restaurant.

As well as being a dining destination for good quality cooking, it also prides itself on its status as a proper pub where you can sink a pint with friends and take advantage of the extensive offering of local real ales, lagers and wines.

The top-notch accommodation is enticing too.

Chef **Sue Hammett**. 3 course lunch from **£28.** 3 course dinner from **£28.** Seats **100.** Bedrooms **9.** Room rate from **£140**

Burgois, St Issey, Padstow, Cornwall, PL27 7QQ
01841 540361
www.pickwick.inn.co.uk

f @thepickwickinn
🐦 @thepickwickinn
📷 @pickwick.inn

139 S

The Old Mill House Bistro

The old-world feel of this 16th century corn mill, complete with working water wheel, is lent picture-book charm by its proximity to an ancient bridge and babbling creek in the Cornish village of Little Petherick.

The family run bistro, headed up by chef Adam Tomlinson, is a relaxed setting in which to enjoy the bounty of the county including pigeon, steak, duck and locally landed seafood. A choice of Cornish wines and gins complements classic dishes and everything, from the crusty tomato and thyme mini loaves to petits fours, is crafted in-house.

Chef **Adam Tomlinson**. 3 course lunch from **£18.** 3 course dinner from **£25.** Seats **24.** Bedrooms **7.** Room rate from **£90**

Little Petherick, Wadebridge, Cornwall, PL27 7QT
01841 540388
www.oldmillbistro.co.uk

f @oldmillpadstow
🐦 @oldmillpadstow
📷 @the_old_mill_house

140 S

Fistral Beach Hotel and Spa

Dishes such as salt and pepper squid, seaweed crusted hake and local cheeseboards provide visitors to this beachside hotel and restaurant with a taste of the Cornish terroir.

Days spent exploring the stunning stretch of coastline or out in the surf end on a sweet high at the Dune Restaurant, where head chef Tom Bennetts fashions picture-perfect dishes using locally sourced and seasonal ingredients. Book a couple's treatment at the spa to unwind before dinner.

Chef **Tom Bennetts**. 3 course lunch from **£22.** 3 course dinner from **£29.** Seats **150.** Bedrooms **71.** Room rate from **£99**

Esplande Road, Newquay, Cornwall, TR7 1PT
01637 852221
www.fistralbeachhotel.co.uk

f @fistralbeachhotel
🐦 @fistralbeachh
📷 @fistralbeachhotel

141

Hooked! Restaurant & Bar

Truro's laid-back dining haunt crafts most of its dishes using seafood from Cornwall's crystalline waters.

Share in the drama and watch tapas being prepped in the open kitchen as the talented team fashion the likes of Falmouth scallops with pork and mustard terrine or Goan seafood curry with jasmine rice.

The result is a winning mix of seasonal and global, peppered with genuine foodie passion and served in contemporary yellow leather-banquette surrounds.

Chefs **Rob Duncan and Joshua Cutlan.** 3 course lunch from **£25.** 3 course dinner from **£25.** Seats **54**

Tabernacle Street, Truro, Cornwall, TR1 2EJ
01872 274700
www.hookedrestaurantandbar.co.uk

f @hookedrestaurantbar
🐦 @hookedtruro
📷 @hookedrestaurantandbar

142

The Watch House

Sure, you could order the steak frites or ricotta ravioli at this chilled St Mawes restaurant but you'd only be enjoying a sliver of the experience, as fresh-off-the-boat seafood is the raison d'être at The Watch House.

Porthilly rock oysters, locally landed crab and Cornwall-smoked salmon are just some of the incredible ingredients which arrive at head chef Will Gould's kitchen door. If you can, grab a window seat and indulge in a lazy afternoon of cracking shells, slurping oysters and sipping a glass of something sparkling. The award winning sustainable fish and chip supper is another must.

Chef **Will Gould.** 3 course lunch from **£25.** 3 course dinner from **£35.** Seats **70**

1 The Square, St Mawes, Truro, Cornwall, TR2 5DJ
01326 270038
www.watchhousestmawes.co.uk

f @thewatchhouse
🐦 @the_watch_house
📷 @the_watchhouse_cornwall

---

143 S

Brasserie on the Bay

Palm-frond-framed sea views come as standard at this Falmouth resort – and those to be savoured from the brasserie are some of the best of all.

Head chef Daniel Kerr crafts striking dishes to complement the idyllic setting and utilises the bountiful natural larder on his kitchen doorstep. The dining experience is further heightened by a pleasing wine list and the option to stay the night in a seaside-chic bedroom. If the previous evening's overindulgence requires a little restoration, soak away a couple of hours in the spa.

Chef **Daniel Kerr.** 3 course lunch from **£26.95.** 3 course dinner from **£36.** Seats **160.** Bedrooms **84.** Room rate from **£110**

St Michaels Resort, Gyllyngvase Beach, Falmouth, Cornwall, TR11 4NB
01326 312707
www.stmichaelshotel.co.uk

f @stmichaelsresort
🐦 @stmichaelshotel
📷 @stmichaelsresort

---

144 S

Meudon Hotel

Eight and a half acres of lush sub-tropical gardens surround Meudon Hotel and lead to its private beach, Bream Cove. And with the South West Coast Path on the doorstep and wild swimming spots close by, the family-run retreat is a playground for nature lovers and weekend adventurers.

Whatever the day's pursuits entail, dinner is guaranteed to be an equally thrilling affair. Head chef Iain Mckay has an abundance of seafood, meat and locally-grown vegetables at his fingertips and works with his skilled team to create dishes to savour.

Chef **Iain Mckay.** 3 course lunch from **£22.50.** 3 course dinner from **£32.** Seats **70.** Bedrooms **30.** Room rate from **£80**

Maenporth Road, Falmouth, Cornwall, TR11 5HT
01326 250541
www.meudon.co.uk

f @meudonhotel
🐦 @meudonhotel
📷 @meudonhotel

145 S

The Bay Hotel

Leave your laptop at home and switch your phone to aeroplane mode, as a weekend at this beautiful bolthole in the fishing village of Coverack is all about disconnecting from the realm of reality.

Watch the wild waters of the Lizard Peninsula lap at the coastline from your window, bask in the Cornish sunshine with a glass of something good on the terrace and then feast on a bounty of locally caught seafood at The Bay's smart restaurant.

Chef **Chris Conboye**. 3 course dinner from **£35.** Seats **38.** Bedrooms **14.** Room rate from **£150**

North Corner, Coverack, Helston, TR12 6TF
01326 280464
www.thebayhotel.co.uk

f @thebayhotelcoverack
🐦 @bayhotelc

147 S

The Bay at Hotel Penzance

Set high above the rooftops of Penzance, this well-established and much-loved hotel restaurant offers staggering views over Mount's Bay.

Head chef Ben Reeve is part of the fabric of the place and has had time and space to develop masterful and individual dishes which show his understanding of Cornish ingredients and appreciation of modern British menus.

Peppering his cooking with an exotic dash of global influences, it's no surprise he's retained two AA rosettes for 14 years.

Chef **Ben Reeve**. 3 course dinner from **£32.** Seats **50.** Bedrooms **25.** Room rate from **£90**

Britons Hill, Penzance, Cornwall, TR18 3AE
01736 363117
www.hotelpenzance.com

f @hotelpenzance
🐦 @perfectpenzance

146 A

The Square at Porthleven

There are many ways to savour this harbourside gem: visit at lunchtime for hearty favourites such as Cornish pork sausage with local greens, hold out for dinner and discover delights including chargrilled flat iron steak and whole Newlyn plaice, or swing by for dinner-to-go from the restaurant's Deli and Ice Cream Emporium.

Whichever you choose, menus change daily and champion the best in local produce, while pretty much everything (drool over the homemade ice cream) is made in-house.

Chef **Bryok Williams**. 3 course lunch from **£22.50.** 3 course dinner from **£24.50.** Seats **40**

7 Fore Street, Porthleven, Helston, Cornwall, TR13 9HQ
01326 573911
www.thesquareatporthleven.co.uk

f @thesquareatporthleven
🐦 @thesquarepl
📷 @thesquarepl

join the club

N°**59**
Number Eight

The Trencherman's Club provides information about exclusive offers and events at Trencherman's restaurants.

It's free and you'll receive the information in a fortnightly email newsletter. Naturally, we won't share your details.

Sign up now at

www.trenchermans-guide.com

Join the conversation

f The Trenchermans Guide

🐦 @trenchermans

📷 @trenchermans_guide

Wine notes

For details of those special wines you've experienced at
Trencherman's restaurants

Wine notes

For details of those special wines you've experienced at
Trencherman's restaurants

Wine notes

For details of those special wines you've experienced at
Trencherman's restaurants

Index

	Entry No		Entry No
2 Fore Street Restaurant	134	Club House, The	43
		Coach House by Michael Caines, The	62
		Cornish Arms, The	83
A		Crab House Cafe, The	55
Abbots Court	42		
Acorn Inn	54	**D–F**	
Acorn Restaurant	27	Dan Moon at The Gainsborough	28
Alexandra Hotel & Restaurant	46	Dining Room, The	137
Alverton, The	115	Dining Room at Saunton, The	60
Angel – Taste of Devon, The	72	Farmers Arms, The	58
Anokaa Restaurant	21	Fig Tree @ 36, The	104
Appleton's Bar & Restaurant	113	Fistral Beach Hotel and Spa	140
Arundell Arms Hotel & Restaurant, The	86	Fontmell, The	51
Augustus	35		
		G	
B		Galley Restaurant, The	68
Barbican Kitchen	77	Gara Rock	102
Bath Priory, The	25	George at Woolley, The	18
Bay at Hotel Penzance, The	147	Gidleigh Park	81
Bay Hotel, The	145	Glazebrook House Hotel	75
BCK Bistro & Bottle Shop	130	Globe, Milverton, The	37
Bell, The	14	Goodfellows	31
Bell Inn, The	5	Greedy Goose, The	78
Boringdon Hall	76	Gylly Beach Cafe	125
Brasserie on the Bay	143		
Brassica Restaurant	45	**H**	
Bunch of Grapes, The	17	Harris's Restaurant	132
		Harvey Nichols Second Floor Restaurant	24
C		Highbullen Hotel Golf and Country Club	92
Calcot & Spa	8	HIX Oyster & Fish House	57
Captain's Club Hotel	40	Hooked! Restaurant & Bar	141
Carlyon Bay Hotel	108	Horn of Plenty, The	84
Chewton Glen Hotel & Spa	48		

Entry No

Horse, The	97
Hotel Endsleigh	85
Howard's House Hotel	16

I–K

Idle Rocks, The	120
Ilsington Country House Hotel and Spa	98
Jamie Oliver's Fifteen Cornwall	114
Koj	10
Kota	128

L

Lamb at Longdown, The	70
Lamb Inn at Sandford, The	94
Lansdowne Strand	19
Lewtrenchard Manor	87
Little Barwick House	33
Lord Poulett Arms, The	34
Lords of the Manor Hotel	1
Lucknam Park Hotel & Spa	11
Lugger, The	117
Luttrell Arms Hotel, The	38
Lympstone Manor	67

M

Masons Arms Knowstone, The	63
Menu Gordon Jones	30
Methuen Arms, The	12
Meudon Hotel	144
Mill End Hotel	96
Mint Room - Bath	29
Mint Room - Bristol	23

Entry No

Mount Haven Hotel and Restaurant	129
Museum Inn, The	50

N

Nare, The	118
New Yard Restaurant	127
NoBody Inn, The	71
Number Eight	59
Nutty Duck at Trevalsa Court, The	136

O

Old Library Restaurant, The	99
Old Mill House Bistro, The	139
Old Passage, The	4
Old Quay House Hotel, The	107
Olive Tree Restaurant, The	26
Oliver's	123
Ollerod, The	44
Outlaw's Fish Kitchen	110

P

Painswick, The	3
Paschoe House	80
Peppermill, The	15
Peter Mundy at The Ginger Peanut	89
Pickwick Inn & Oliver's Restaurant, The	138
Plumber Manor	52
Porthminster Beach Cafe	131
Pyne Arms	88

Index

Q–R

Queens Arms, The	32
Rams Head Inn and Country Hotel, The	93
Rastella at Merchants Manor	124
Restaurant Nathan Outlaw	109
Rick Stein, Sandbanks	41
Rising Sun, The	36
Riviera Hotel and Restaurant, The	65
Rock Inn, The	90
Rock Salt Cafe	79
Rodean Restaurant	95
Rosevine Hotel, The	119
Royal Castle Hotel, The	101
Royal Duchy Hotel, The	126
Royal George, The	91
Royal Seven Stars, The	100

S

Salcombe Harbour Hotel & Spa	103
Salutation Inn, The	69
Sardine Factory Restaurant, The	135
Saveur	66
Seafood Restaurant, The	111
Seagrave Arms, The	9
Seasons, The Eastbury Hotel	53
Shore Restaurant, The	133
Slaughters Manor House, The	2
Soar Mill Cove Hotel	74
Spiny Lobster Grill, The	22
Springer Spaniel, The	105
Square at Porthleven, The	146

St Petroc's Bistro	112
Star & Garter	122
Station Kitchen, The	56
Swan, The	64

T

Tabb's Restaurant	116
Talland Bay Hotel	106
Three Lions, The	39
Three Tuns Freehouse	20
Twenty_Seven by Jamie Rogers	73
Two Bridges Hotel	82

W–Y

Watch House, The	142
Water's Edge at The Greenbank Hotel, The	121
Watersmeet Hotel	61
WestBeach Restaurant	49
White Horse Inn, The	13
Wild Garlic	6
Wilder	7
Yew Tree, The	47

TRENCHERMAN'S
GUIDE

EDITION

27